TRON: LEGACY – THE GRAPHIC NOVEL

Manuscript Adaptation: Stefano Amb
Layout and Ink: Paolo Mottura
Ink: Michela Frare
Paint: Slava Panarin (Creative Consultant), V liy Shus Stefania Acquaro
Paint Coordination: Tomatofarm
Paint Supervision: Stefano Attardi, Giorgio Vallorani
Design: Olga Norman & Larissa Soffientini at Pocko (Editorial Design)
Nicola Schwartz (Creative Consultant)
Editing: Litomilano S.r.l., Pocko
Contributors: Marco Ghiglione, Cristina Giorgilli, Claudio Sciarrone, Elisabetta Sedda,
Paola Beretta, Marta De Cunto, Tommaso Guaita

Based on the screenplay by Eddy Kitsis & Adam Horowitz
Executive Producer: Donald Kushner
Produced by Sean Bailey, Jeffrey Silver, Steven Lisberger
Directed by Joseph Kosinski
Created by Disney Publishing Worldwide - Global Magazine Editorial Team:
Bianca Coletti (Editorial Director)
Roberto Santillo (Creative Director)
Guido Frazzini (Director Franchise Editorial Development – project supervisor)

Special thanks to:
Sean Bailey, Justin Springer, Dominique Flynn, Dale Kennedy, Erik Schmudde

 Published by Panini Publishing, a division of Panini UK. Office of publication: Panini UK, Brockbourne House, 77 Mount Ephraim, Tunbridge Wells, Kent TN4 8BS.

ISBN: 978-1-8465

Printed in the UK

PROLOGUE

BY JAI NITZ & JEFF MATSUDA

I AM DUMONT, THE KEEPER OF RECORDS, THE KEEPER OF INFORMATION, THE ORDAINED STORYTELLER OF FLYNN, THE CREATOR. IT IS HIS WILL THAT I RECORD THIS INFORMATION FOR HIS DISC.
FLYNN'S STORY BEGINS IN THE WORLD OF THE USERS, A CITY OF ANGELS AND LIGHTS.
FLYNN'S FIRST ACT WAS TO MAKE LIGHT IN OUR WORLD OF DARKNESS. HE BUILT US, BIT BY BIT.
FLYNN WAS UNLIKE THE OTHER USERS. HE WAS, AND IS, A CREATOR. HE MADE ORDER FROM THE CHAOS OF ONES AND ZEROES.
HIS FINEST CREATION, THE MASTER CONTROL PROGRAM, REBELLED AND TRIED TO DESTROY HIM. THE MCP BROUGHT FLYNN TO THE GRID.

ONCE HERE, THE MCP TASKED THE SARK PROGRAM TO HAVE FLYNN KILLED IN THE GAMES OF HIS OWN CREATION.
THE MCP BELIEVED IN IRONY. NO SMALL FEAT FOR A COMPUTER PROGRAM, MIND YOU.
SARK, FOR HIS ENTHUSIASM AND CRUELTY, WAS STILL SCARED OF A USER. BUT SARK FOLLOWED ORDERS.
FLYNN WAS TAKEN TO THE GAMES.

FLYNN WAS A FAST LEARNER, AND SOON DOMINATED THE GAMES.
AND FLYNN WAS NO PROGRAM. HE HAD FREE WILL. HE WAS DEFIANT.
DEFIANT IN THE FACE OF SARK AND THE MCP.
BUT SARK WAS CRUEL AND OBEDIENT.

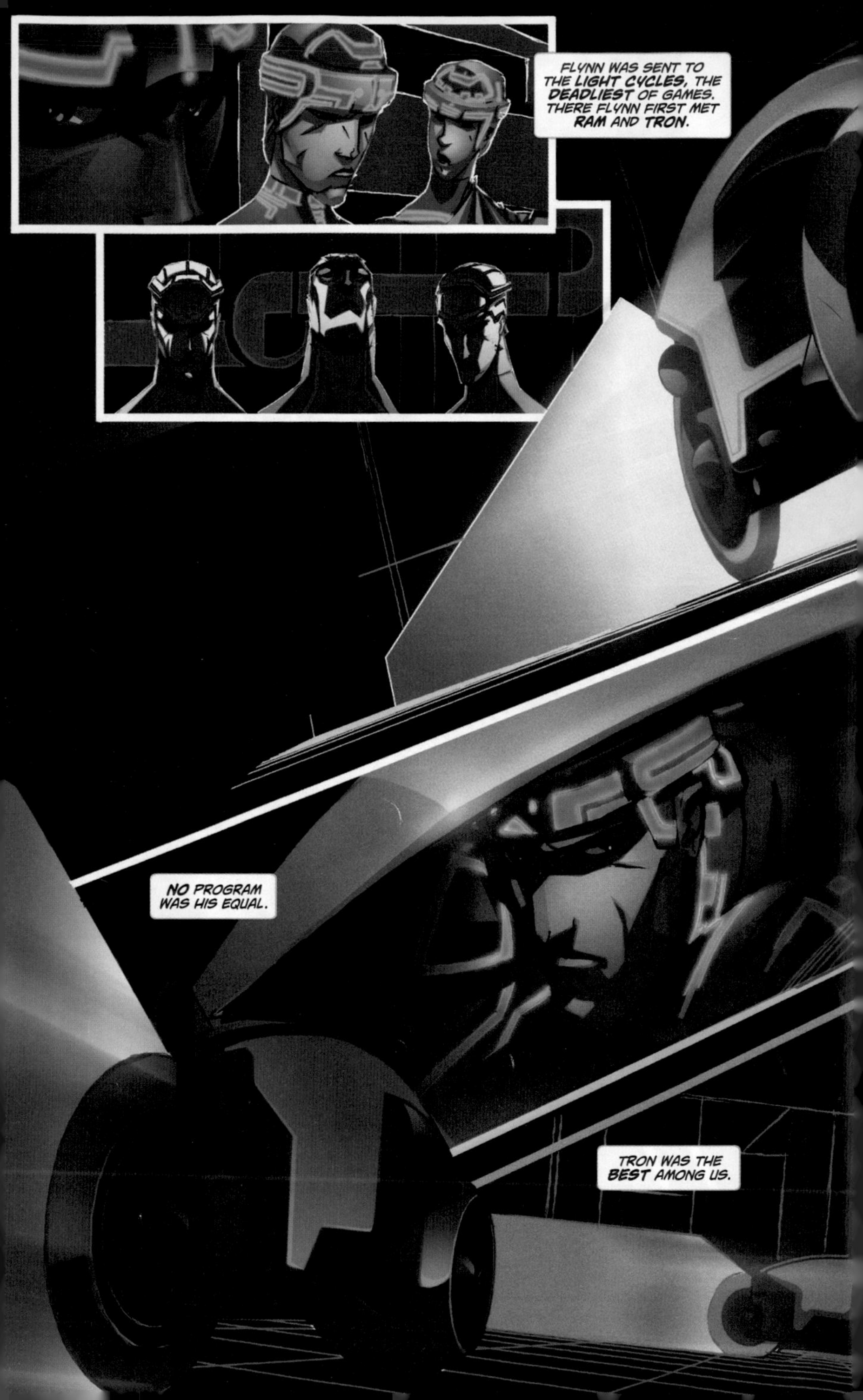
FLYNN WAS SENT TO THE LIGHT CYCLES, THE DEADLIEST OF GAMES. THERE FLYNN FIRST MET RAM AND TRON.
NO PROGRAM WAS HIS EQUAL.
TRON WAS THE BEST AMONG US.

THERE THEY WOULD RACE FOR THEIR LIVES.
FLYNN GOT THE CHANCE TO SEE TRON'S SKILL FIRSTHAND.
THOUGH, SOME WOULD HAVE TO LEARN THE HARD WAY.

TRON AND RAM HELPED FLYNN ESCAPE OUT OF THE GAMES AND ONTO THE GRID. BUT FLYNN'S OWN CREATIONS, THE TANK PROGRAMS, WOULD HUNT THEM DOWN.
FLYNN CREATED THE TANKS TO SERVE AS PROTECTORS OF THE INTEGRITY OF THE GRID.
LITTLE DID HE KNOW THAT HE WOULD ONE DAY BE THE OBJECT OF THEIR WRATH.
FLYNN AND RAM WERE HIT, THEIR LIGHT CYCLES DESTROYED. TRON BELIEVED THEM TO BE DEAD.

BUT FLYNN WAS MORE RESILIENT THAN MOST. HE CARRIED RAM TO THE SAFETY OF A JUNK HEAP.
MEANWHILE, TRON WENT TO HIS COUNTERPART, YORI.
THEY DECIDED TO TAKE ON THE MCP THEMSELVES.

FLYNN DISPLAYED HIS POWER AND RECONSTRUCTED A RECOGNIZER FROM SCRAP.

WHILE TRON AND YORI HEADED TO THE I/O TOWER FOR HELP.

FLYNN REVEALED HIS TRUE NATURE TO RAM, BUT IT WAS TOO LATE. RAM DID NOT SURVIVE, AND FLYNN LEARNED THE VALUE OF LIFE HERE ON THE GRID.

TRON AND YORI CAME BEFORE ME, AND ASKED TO SPEAK TO THE USERS FOR A WAY TO DEFEAT THE MCP.

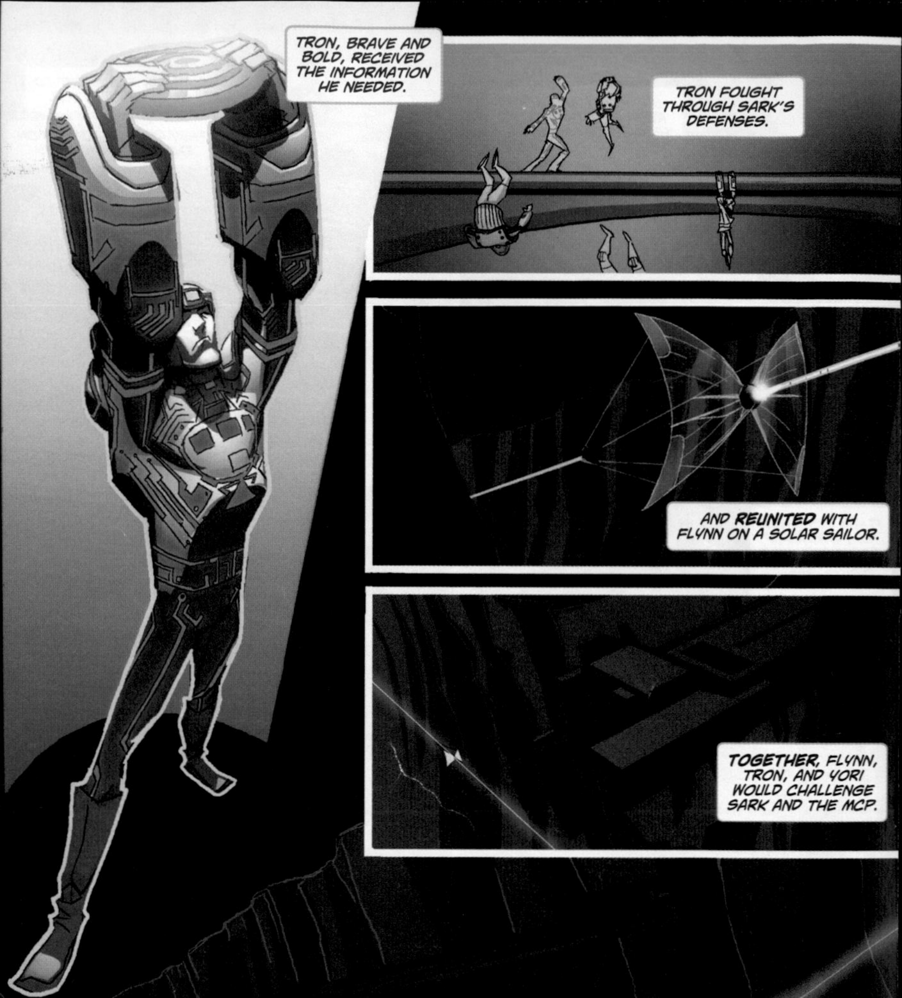
TRON, BRAVE AND BOLD, RECEIVED THE INFORMATION HE NEEDED.
TRON FOUGHT THROUGH SARK'S DEFENSES.
AND REUNITED WITH FLYNN ON A SOLAR SAILOR.
TOGETHER, FLYNN, TRON, AND YORI WOULD CHALLENGE SARK AND THE MCP.

BUT IT WOULD COME TO PASS THAT TRON'S DESIRE FOR FREEDOM COULD NOT BE QUELLED.
AND SARK'S CRUELTY WOULD NOT RELENT.
AND WHEN THEY FINALLY MET...
THE PASSION FOR FREEDOM WON OUT.

BUT THE MCP WAS A POWERFUL BEING. SARK WAS REBUILT AND REBORN WITH ENOUGH POWER TO OVERWHELM EVEN TRON.
THE MCP HAD NOT PREPARED FOR FLYNN. IT HAD NOT PREPARED FOR THE CREATOR AND HIS GLORY. FLYNN CAST HIMSELF INTO THE MCP.
FLYNN CREATED A HOLE IN THE MCP'S DEFENSES, AND TRON STRUCK.

THE INFORMATION ON TRON'S DISC DESTROYED THE MCP, AND THE SYSTEM WAS FOREVER CHANGED.
THE OPPRESSIVE RED OF THE MCP GAVE WAY TO THE NEW BLUE BEAM OF FLYNN. AND FLYNN WAS RESTORED TO HIS USER FORM.
IN THE WORLD OF THE USERS, FLYNN REGAINED CONTROL OVER THE SYSTEM.
ENC
THE CREATOR, RETURNED TO HIS CITY OF USERS, WOULD GRACE US OFTEN. HIS GUIDANCE AND STEWARDSHIP USHERED IN A NEW ERA. AND SO ENDS THE GOSPEL ACCORDING TO DUMONT, THE GOSPEL OF FLYNN'S DISC.

+

CHAPTER ONE

BY JAI NITZ, STARLIGHT RUNNER ENTERTAINMENT,
ANDIE TONG, & PETE PANTAZIS

THIS IS WHERE I SAW THEM LAST, TRON.
I CAN SEE THE BUGS NOW, FLYNN.
ROME WASN'T BUILT IN A DAY.

SO MANY OF THEM. WHERE DID THEY COME FROM?
YEAH, I'M STILL WORKING ON THAT.
THEY'RE GAINING ON US!

OH CRAP.

THE ROAD AHEAD IS DISINTEGRATING TOO.
WE'RE GONNA NEED TO GO OFF-ROAD.
DON'T WORRY...
...THIS IS GONNA BE GOOD.

THOOM
THE ROMAN EMPIRE STARTED AS A COLLECTION OF HUTS ON TOP OF SEVEN HILLS THAT OVERLOOKED A RIVER VALLEY.

THAT RIVER AND THE NATURAL SURROUNDINGS MADE ROME SAFE AND STRONG. IT HAD SOME HICCUPS ALONG THE WAY, BUT IT GREW AND GREW.

YOU ALL RIGHT?
YEAH, YOU?
IT GREW INTO AN EMPIRE. IT BECAME THE CULTURAL CENTER OF THE WORLD AND THE BIRTHPLACE OF WESTERN SOCIETY.
ARE YOU KIDDING?

I'M HAVING THE TIME OF MY LIFE, MAN.
BUT THE GRIDBUGS.
THEY'RE A PROBLEM, BUT NOTHING YOU CAN'T PROTECT US FROM.
YOU KEEP THE GRID SAFE, AND SHADDOX AND THE OTHERS WILL RUN THE PROJECTS AND THE GAMES.
BUT YOUR VERY PRESENCE IS REQUIRED TO HELP BRING ORDER FROM THE CHAOS.
DON'T SELL YOURSELF SHORT, BUDDY. YOU'RE DOING FINE.

I BROUGHT YOU HERE FROM THE OLD SYSTEM BECAUSE YOU'RE THE BEST SECURITY FORCE A GUY COULD HAVE.
AND YOU?
I'LL LOOK FURTHER INTO THE INSTABILITIES FROM THE OUTSIDE.
IT ROSE AND FELL AND ROSE AGAIN AS SOMETHING NEW.
ZZZING

TIME?
SEVEN FORTY-SEVEN. AM.
OH YEAH? I'VE GOT THE WHOLE DAY AHEAD OF ME. WAIT, WHAT DAY IS IT?
TUESDAY, APRIL SEVEN-TEENTH.
TUESDAY? YIKES. TUESDAY, TUESDAY...
CALENDAR, AGENDA, SEVENTEENTH OF APRIL.
DOCTOR APPOINTMENT. EIGHT AM. DOCTOR SPRINGER.
JORDAN.

MANY OF THE BUILDING BLOCKS OF SOCIETY COME FROM ROME. FOR INSTANCE, THE CONCEPT OF MEDICAL CARE BEING AVAILABLE TO ALL CASTES, NOT JUST THE WEALTHY, COMES FROM ROME.
SKREEET
HI, I'M KEVIN FLYNN, I HAVE AN APPOINTMENT...
...WE HAVE AN APPOINTMENT...
...I MEAN, JORDAN CANAS HAS AN APPOINTMENT WITH DOCTOR SPRINGER.
MISS CANAS WILL BE...
OH, HEY BABE. SORRY, I GOT HUNG UP ON SOME BUGS IN THE SYSTEM. I NEED SOMETHING BIGGER THAN THE RESOURCE DISTRIBUTION PROGRAM. I'M REALLY SORRY, I JUST...
KEVIN FLYNN, YOU'VE NEVER BEEN ON TIME FOR ANYTHING IN YOUR LIFE. BESIDES, I CAN'T BE MAD AT YOU NOW.
NOT WITH THIS.
April 1983

WOW, A BOY?
IT'S PRETTY HARD TO MISS, KEVIN.

YOU SHOULD HAVE SEEN IT. IT WAS MAGICAL.
IT JUST LOOKS SO GRAINY AND FUZZY.
I'M USED TO BETTER GRAPHICS. SOMEONE REALLY SHOULD INVENT A BETTER SONOGRAM CAMERA.

WELL, WHEN YOU'RE DONE WITH YOUR CURRENT OBSESSION, YOU CAN MAKE THAT YOUR NEXT PRIORITY.
FOR *YOU*, ANYTHING.

ENCOM
EVEN GRAINY AND FUZZY, IT WAS BEYOND ANYTHING I'VE EVER SEEN. IT'S A NEW LIFE. IT'S JUST... BEYOND ANYTHING I COULD EXPRESS.
I KNOW WHAT YOU MEAN.

YOU'RE LATE.
YOU SHOULD HAVE SEEN IT, ALAN. IT WAS AMAZING.
I'M SURE IT WAS. YOUR PROGRAMS ALWAYS ARE AMAZING, KEVIN. HOW WAS THE SONOGRAM?
ENCOM
I GOTTA TELL YOU, THAT WAS PRETTY AWESOME TOO.
THE BOARD IS GETTING ANTSY. YOU GO OFF THE GRID FOR DAYS AT A TIME; NO ONE CAN CONTACT YOU. I CAN'T FIND YOU.
LOOK, KEVIN, THEY'RE IN THE BUSINESS OF BEING IN BUSINESS. THEY DON'T GET EXCITED BY PROGRAMMING BREAKTHROUGHS THE WAY YOU AND I DO. THEY ARE EXCITED ABOUT A HEALTHY BOTTOM LINE.
MANY OF THE LESSONS ABOUT HOW A SOCIETY DESTROYS ITSELF COME FROM ROME. IF YO TAKE THE HISTORY BOOKS AT FACE VALUE, ALMOST EVERYONE IS "FROM" ROME.
THEY AREN'T CREATIVE. THEY STILL LEAVE THAT TO YOU. BUT THEY'RE WORRIED ABOUT THEIR GOLDEN GOOSE.
YOU KNOW, GETTING CONTROL OF ENCOM WAS A LOT MORE FUN THAN RUNNING THE JOINT.

NO ONE IS FROM THE WEST COAST. AT LEAST, IT SEEMS THAT WAY.
ALMOST EVERYONE HERE IS FROM SOMEWHERE ELSE.

TOMORROW'S SCHEDULE?
CONFLICTING APPOINTMENTS, SIR. YOU ARE DOUBLE-BOOKED AT NINE, TEN, ONE, TWO, AND FOUR O'CLOCK.
NOT ME. I WAS BORN AND RAISED HERE.
LOOKS LIKE I NEED TO BE IN TWO PLACES AT ONCE.

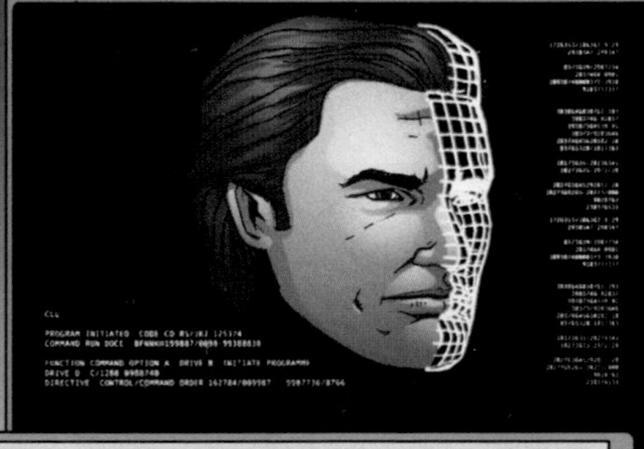

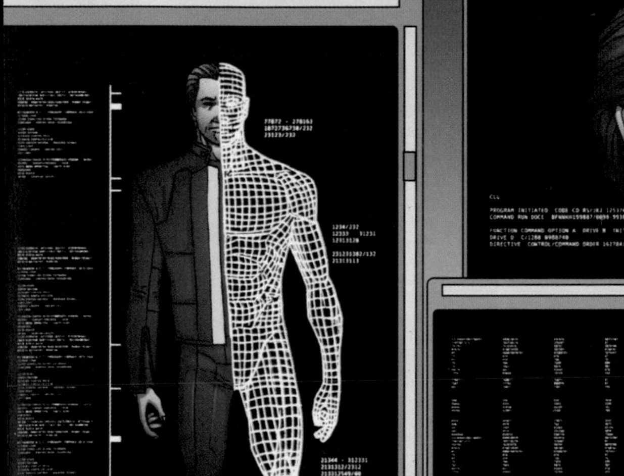

AND IF THIS DIAGNOSTIC CHECKS OUT, I FINALLY WILL BE.
CLU, YOU AND I ARE GOING TO CREATE THE PERFECT SYSTEM.

I HAD TO LEAVE THE MAIN CITY FOR THIS.
CREATING SOMETHING THIS UNIQUE COULD TEAR THE GRID APART.
SO I'M GOING TO HAVE TO GET THIS RIGHT THE FIRST TIME...

YOU ARE TO CREATE THE PERFECT SYSTEM.
TOGETHER, YOU AND I ARE GOING TO CHANGE THE WORLD.

ROME WASN'T BUILT IN A DAY, BUT I WAS.
FLYNN ALWAYS SAID HE BUILT ME IN A DAY. NOT SURE IF I BELIEVE HIM, THOUGH.
THESE ARE MY SEVEN HILLS.
THE BIGGEST CITIES ON THE WEST COAST, LIKE ROME, WERE STARTED ATOP A SERIES OF HILLS ALONG THE WATER.
SAN DIEGO.
LOS ANGELES.
SAN FRANCISCO.
SEATTLE.
SURFING, ENTERTAINMENT, POLITICAL CHANGE, AND MUSIC-- ALL OF THEM MAKE UP CULTURAL CENTERS OF THE NEW WORLD.

I'VE NEVER UNDERSTOOD WHAT A "DAY" WAS. IT TOOK ME MANY CYCLES BEFORE I ACCEPTED FLYNN SPEAKING IN HIS IDIOMS.
BUT I LEARNED AT HIS FEET, AND NOW LOOK AT WHAT I'VE BUILT IN HIS HONOR. OR SHOULD I SAY, WHAT WE'VE BUILT IN HIS HONOR, SHADDOX?
WE'VE DONE WELL, CLU. THE MIND THAT BUILT THE GRID WAS FLYNN'S BUT THE HAND WAS YOURS.
WE'RE ALL WORKING TOWARDS THE SAME GOAL, SHADDOX.
I STATE THE FACTS.

SPEAKING OF THE FACTS...
GAMMA SECTOR HAS A DATA BOTTLE-NECK.
EXPAND THE FORWARD DATA TRACK.
ZETA SECTOR HAS AN ENERGY FLOW PROBLEM AT THE PROGRAM NEXUS.
BEGIN CONSTRUCTION ON ANOTHER ENERGY AQUEDUCT FROM THE TERMINUS TO THE NEXUS. THAT SHOULD DO THE TRICK.
SIGMA SECTOR HAS A FOOT TRAFFIC ISSUE.
SIGMA SECTOR? THE STADIUM? WHAT KIND OF FOOT TRAFFIC ISSUE?
THERE'S TOO MUCH OF IT. THEY CAN'T STAY AWAY FROM HIM.
I SHOULD HAVE KNOWN. TRON.
FLYNN GAVE HIM THE TASK OF CLEANING UP THE OUTSKIRTS OF THE GRID AND KEEPING THE RESIDENTS SAFE. THE GRID IS SAFE, BUT I THINK HE'S QUITE ATTACHED TO THE GAMES.

MANY CYCLES PASSED, AND THE GAMES BECAME MORE AND MORE COMPLEX.
THE GRID WAS MY CULTURAL CENTER OF ELECTRONIC ENTERTAINMENT.

THE WEST COAST MAKES MOVIES AND VIDEO GAMES.

IT BUILDS FANTASY WORLDS THAT PEOPLE USE TO ESCAPE THEIR REGULAR LIVES.
BUT I'VE CREATED THE GREATEST TESTING GROUNDS ANYONE HAS EVER SEEN.
MY FANTASY WORLD IS THE NEW REALITY.

BOLD.
BOLD AND WISE. YOUR MOVE TO GAIN POSITION ON THE LOOP WAS INSPIRED.
I DON'T FEEL VERY INSPIRED RIGHT NOW, SIR.
I WAS LUCKY TO WIN.
I LOOK FORWARD TO COMPETING AGAINST YOU AGAIN.
WHERE I COME FROM, THESE FIGHTS ENDED WHEN ONE OF US WAS DEREZZED.
THE WINNER OF THE RACE, TRON!
I THINK YOU'LL AGREE THAT FLYNN'S VERSION OF THE GAMES ARE FAR SUPERIOR.

CONGRATULATIONS ON THE WIN, TRON. YOUR PRESENCE IS REQUIRED ON THE SURVEY PLATFORM.
CLU?
ON MY WAY!
SCREEE

TOOK YOU LONG ENOUGH, TRON!
FLYNN!

IT'S BEEN TOO LONG, OLD FRIEND.
FLYNN AND I WANT YOUR TAKE ON A... UNIQUE SITUATION.

YEAH, CHECK THIS OUT.
WE WERE AT THE EDGE OF THE CITY. I CAME BACK IN TO TRY AND WORK OUT SOME NEW GAME VARIATIONS... AND THEN... THIS HAPPENED.
INSTEAD OF EVERYONE INSIDE BEING CREATED FROM SOMEWHERE ELSE, NOW THE GRID HAD CITIZENS OF ITS OWN.

WHAT IS THAT?
BACK UP, GUYS! GIVE HER ROOM.
NOT WHAT. *WHO*. HER NAME'S OPHELIA. SHE PICKED IT HERSELF! SHE PICKED HER OWN NAME, MAN!
YOU DIDN'T CREATE THIS PROGRAM? HOW IS THAT POSSIBLE?
SHE'S NOT A PROGRAM. WELL, I MEAN, SHE IS A PROGRAM, BUT SHE'S AN ISOMORPHIC ALGORITHM. SHE'S A NEW LIFE FORM, MAN. SELF-CREATED!
THE LOGIC'S MESSY, AND I HAVE *NO* IDEA HOW THIS HAPPENED YET, BUT IT'S INCREDIBLE! THIS IS THE BEGINNING OF SOMETHING MORE *AMAZING* THAN I THOUGHT WAS POSSIBLE.
I AGREE, BUT I THINK THE POTENTIAL RAMIFICATIONS TO THE GRID GO DEEPER THAN THAT, FLYNN.

CLU, I KNOW I MADE YOU TO KEEP THE GRID RUNNING ORDERLY AND NONE OF THAT HAS CHANGED. IF THIS CONTINUES, I THINK I'M GONNA NEED YOUR HELP MORE THAN EVER.
FLYNN, UNCERTAINTY UPSETS THE NATURAL ORDER OF THE GRID.
SOMETIMES THINGS DEVELOP ON THEIR OWN, CLU. WE NEED TO PROTECT THESE ISOMORPHIC...THESE ISOS. EVERYONE ON THE GRID GETS THAT CHANCE.
THIS IS AMAZING! BUT I HAVE TO GET BACK HOME BEFORE I'M LATE AGAIN, I'LL BE BACK SOON.
THE CREATION OF A NEW LIFE FORM. THE MOST EXCITED I HAVE EVER SEEN HIM. AND HE STILL LEAVES...

"WHAT COULD POSSIBLY BE SO INTERESTING ON THE OTHER SIDE?"
ENCOM
THE TOKYO NUMBERS ARE BOOMING, BUT IT'S TOO SMALL A PORTION OF OUR BUSINESS FOR US TO PROPERLY CAPITALIZE ON IT.
CAN YOU EXPLAIN WHY WE AREN'T MORE HEAVILY INVESTED THERE, MR. FLYNN?
I CAN ANSWER THAT. KEVIN THOUGHT...
NO OFFENSE, MR. BRADLEY, BUT I WAS ASKING MR. FLYNN FOR A REASON.
LIKE MY OWN LIFE, THINGS CHANGED.
OUR REYKJAVIK NUMBERS ARE STAGNANT. WE DON'T HAVE NUMBERS FROM MANILA OR AMSTERDAM. OUR MUMBAI INVESTMENTS ARE LOSING MONEY.
MUMBAI IS THE NEXT BIG THING.
SO SAYS MR. FLYNN, BUT THE MONEY DOESN'T LIE. WE'RE TAKING A BATH IN MUMBAI.
MR. FLYNN, ARE YOU EVEN PAYING ATTENTION?
HMM?

I TOOK CARE OF EVERYTHING AT THE FURNITURE STORE FOR THE NURSERY. YOU DON'T HAVE TO PICK IT UP, YOU DON'T HAVE TO PUT IT TOGETHER, YOU JUST NEED TO MAKE SURE IT'S SIGNED FOR.
UH HUH.
DID YOU BUY THAT MOBILE WE TALKED ABOUT?
NO, BUT I WILL. IS THE PAINT ALL DRY? I WORRY ABOUT THE FUMES.
THE FUMES ONLY LAST FOR A FEW DAYS, KEVIN. THEY'LL BE GONE BY THE TIME THE BABY GETS HERE.
OKAY, IT'S JUST... I WORRY.
KEVIN, BABIES HAVE BEEN BORN WITH LESS TECHNOLOGY FOR THE LAST TEN THOUSAND YEARS. YOU DON'T NEED TO WORRY ABOUT ANYTHING.
THAT'S JUST IT. I FEEL SO RESPONSIBLE FOR THIS. FOR US.
TRON
JUST BE HERE. THAT'S ALL I ASK.
MR. FLYNN? LORA BAINES IS HERE.
I GOTTA RUN, BABE. I'LL CALL YOU BEFORE I LEAVE FOR HOME.

I'M SORRY, MISS BAINES. HE'S ON THE PHONE WITH HIS...
LORA? GEEZ, BETTY, WHY DIDN'T YOU SAY SO!
HI. LISTEN, I WANTED TO TELL YOU IN PERSON.
I'M LEAVING, KEVIN.
WHAT?
IT'S A JOB IN WASHINGTON, ONE THAT I CAN'T PASS UP.
ARE YOU SURE? WHAT ABOUT ALAN?
ALAN AND I ARE STAYING TOGETHER. WE'LL MAKE IT WORK.
LORA, I'M SO SORRY. ALAN SAID YOU WANTED SOME FACE TIME, BUT I'VE BEEN SO BUSY WITH MY... RESEARCH.
KEVIN, I'VE KNOWN YOU LONGER THAN ANYONE AT THIS COMPANY. I KNOW HOW BUSY YOU GET. I KNOW HOW GOOD YOU'VE BEEN TO ME AND ALAN.
SORRY TO INTERRUPT YOU, MR. FLYNN. IT'S YOUR WIFE, SHE SAYS IT'S URGENT...

"...SHE SAID IT'S ABOUT THE BABY."
OH NO...LOOK OUT!
RUMBLE
RUN!
ZWANG
I USED TO BE ABOUT MAKING GAMES AND HAVING FUN. THAT ALL CHANGED.

LOOK! IT'S HIM!
EVERYONE REMAIN CALM. I'VE GOT THIS UNDER CONTROL.

IS EVERYONE ALL RIGHT?
THANKS TO YOU, TRON.

THE GRIDBUGS WAVES ARE BACK IN GREATER NUMBERS AND *ONLY* IN THE ISO SECTIONS OF THE GRID. BUT WHERE ARE THEY COMING FROM?
YOU AND FLYNN SOLVED THE GRIDBUG PROBLEM HUNDREDS OF CYCLES AGO. WHY IS THIS HAPPENING?
I DON'T KNOW, OPHELIA. BUT FLYNN TASKED US WITH KEEPING YOU SAFE.
CLU AND I WILL FIGURE IT OUT.
I DON'T HAVE AN ANSWER FOR YOU, TRON.

WE DON'T KNOW WHY OR HOW THE GRIDBUGS HAVE RESURFACED.
OR WHY THE BUGS ARE LOCALIZED TO THE ISO SECTIONS OF THE GRID?
THAT IS A QUESTION I HAVE AN ANSWER TO. HAS IT OCCURRED TO YOU THAT THE ISOS THEMSELVES MIGHT ATTRACT OR EVEN CAUSE GRIDBUGS?
THINK ABOUT IT. THEY ARE THE VERY DEFINITION OF UNCERTAINTY. THE BUGS ARE A PRODUCT OF UNCERTAINTY.
SHADDOX? WHAT DO YOU THINK?
I THINK IT'S A PROBLEM WE NEED FLYNN TO ADDRESS AS SOON AS WE CAN.

YES, TRON, IT'S A PROBLEM. BUT I THINK WE NEED TO START THINKING MORE AMBITIOUSLY.
I DON'T THINK THE PROBLEM HAS GOTTEN BEYOND MY ABILITY TO HANDLE.
FOR NOW. THE PROBLEM HASN'T GOTTEN BEYOND YOUR ABILITIES TO HANDLE FOR NOW. HOW LONG CAN YOU MAINTAIN THAT? ONE CYCLE? TEN?
HOW MANY CYCLES HAS IT BEEN SINCE WE'VE HEARD FROM FLYNN? HIS TIES TO HIS "REAL WORLD" DISTRACT HIM FROM OUR NEEDS.
HIS DEPARTURE HAS BEEN TOO PROLONGED FOR US TO IGNORE IT ANY LONGER.
SO WE WAIT?
I SAID I THOUGHT THE GRIDBUGS WERE A PROBLEM, CLU. I DID NOT SUGGEST A DEVIATION FROM THE CREATOR'S WISHES.
HOW LONG? SHADDOX? TRON? HOW LONG BEFORE WE TAKE OUR DESTINY IN OUR OWN HANDS?
FLYNN WANTS THIS WORLD TO BE EVERYTHING IT CAN BE. I, OBVIOUSLY, WANT THE SAME THING. WE CAN LIVE UP TO HIS DREAMS, BUT WE CAN'T JUST WAIT FOREVER.

"WHAT IF OUR CREATOR ISN'T COMING BACK?"

KEVIN?
JORDAN?! I'M COMING!

EVERYTHING OKAY, BABE? WHAT'S WRONG? WHAT CAN I DO?
CALM DOWN, TIGER. I JUST NEED THE HOT WATER BOTTLE REHEATED.
KEVIN, YOU KNOW, YOU CAN GO TO WORK. I COULD GET ANDREA TO STAY WITH ME.

YOU NEED ME HERE. BESIDES, THEY'RE GROWNUPS; THEY CAN MAKE IT WITHOUT ME FOR A FEW WEEKS.
HONEY, IT WAS A SCARE, AND IT WAS WEEKS AGO. EVERYTHING'S GOING TO BE OKAY.
THEY DON'T LIKE HOW I RUN THINGS ANYWAY. LET'S SEE THEM TRY.
I'M NOT BLIND. YOU'RE GOING CRAZY AT HOME AND SOMEONE CALLS EVERY FEW MINUTES AS IT IS. I KNOW ALAN CAME BY LAST NIGHT.
WHY DON'T YOU GET OUT OF THE HOUSE FOR A WHILE AND WORK ON SOME NEW IDEAS. I KNOW YOU HAVE THEM, YOU ALWAYS DO, AND IT'S BEEN A WHILE SINCE YOU'VE MENTIONED THE GAMES.
BUT YOU NEED ME HERE. I NEED TO BE AROUND.
I NEED YOU TO BE YOU, KEVIN FLYNN.
MAKE ME PROUD. AND DON'T DISAPPEAR ON ME.
ACTUALLY, I'VE BEEN WORKING ON THAT, BABE. MWAH.

BZZT

GOTCHA!

JORDAN, I FINALLY GOT IT TO WORK. NOW YOU CAN...

...CALL ME.
I WANTED TO HAVE FUN. I WANTED OTHER PEOPLE TO HAVE FUN. THAT WAS THE GRID'S ORIGIN. BUT NOW IT'S MORE THAN THAT.

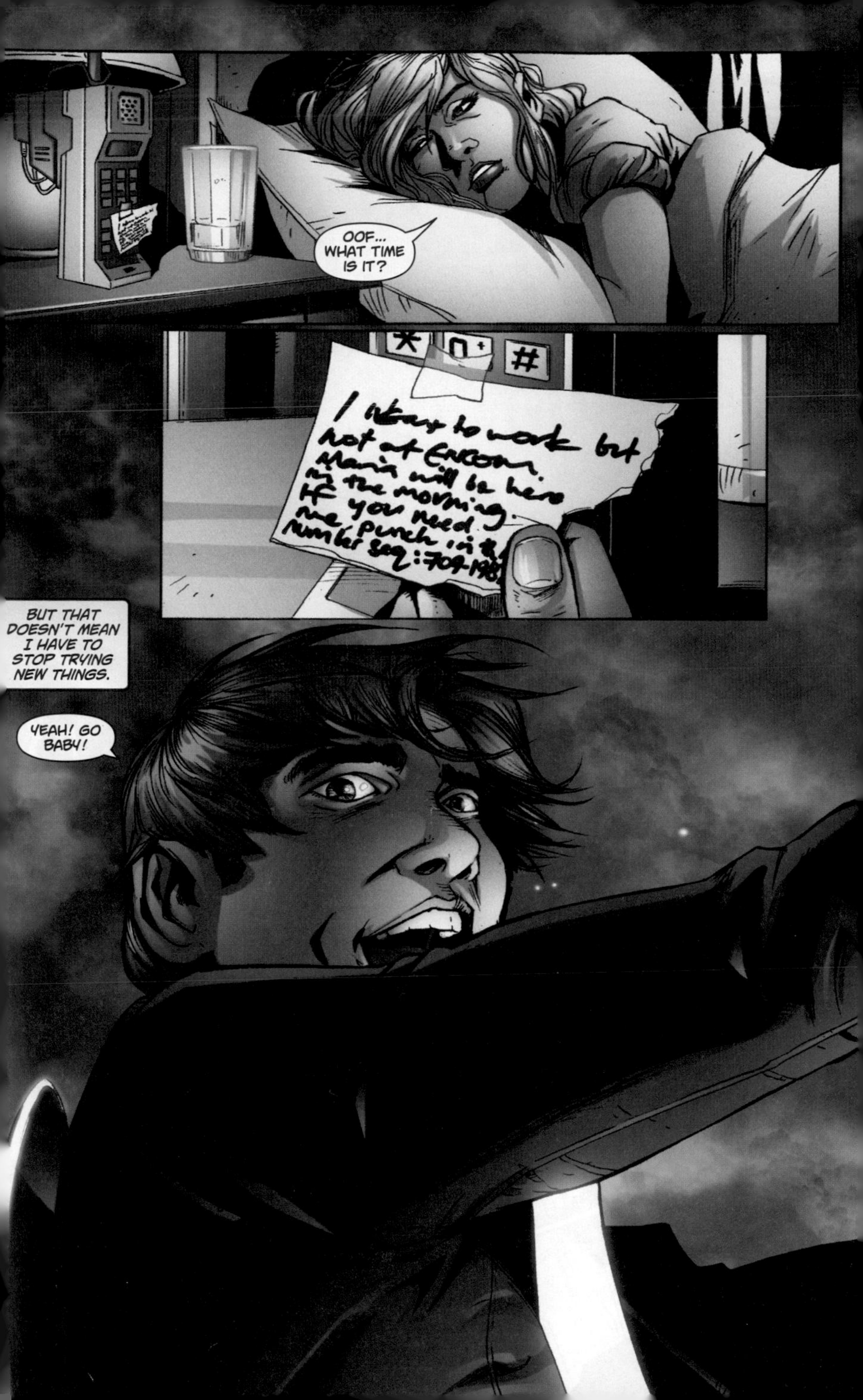
OOF... WHAT TIME IS IT?
BUT THAT DOESN'T MEAN I HAVE TO STOP TRYING NEW THINGS.
YEAH! GO BABY!

GO GO GO!

YES YES YES!
YES YES.
THAT DOESN'T MEAN I DON'T STILL MAKE MISTAKES.
THAT'S WHY I BUILT THIS PLACE. TO TEST THINGS. TO GIVE EVERYTHING I MADE A SECOND CHANCE. GIVEN SOME TIME, AMAZING THINGS HAVE HAPPENED HERE.
YES?
NO NO NO!

BOOOM
DON'T WORRY, I'VE GOT YOU.

I HEARD REPORTS OF A CRAZY NEW INVENTION ON THE GRID BEFORE I EVEN SAW THE PORTAL LIGHT UP.
HELLO, FLYNN.
HI. AND I WAS NEVER IN DANGER, TRON.
NOTHING TO SEE HERE, FOLKS. PLEASE DISPERSE.
THE CREATOR!
HE'S BACK!
IT IS GOOD TO HAVE YOU BACK, FLYNN. WE'VE HAD SOME PROBLEMS SINCE YOU LEFT.
THE SUSTAINED AND INCREASED PRESENCE OF THE ISOS HAS TRIGGERED SOME SYSTEM GLITCHES.
NO PROBLEM. WE'LL JUST RUN A DIAGNOSTIC. WHAT KIND OF...
...GLITCH?

GET DOWN!
ZWAM
THAT SHOULDN' HAVE HAPPENED
THE GRID IS HAVING... DIFFICULTIES... ACCEPTING NEW PROGRAMS.
THEN LET'S FI 'EM.

CLU, ARE YOU ACTUALLY MAD AT ME?
DID YOU EVEN PROGRAM ME TO GET ANGRY, FLYNN? I AM FRUSTRATED BY MY FAITH. I HAVE HELD MY FAITH IN YOU AND TRIED TO DO WHAT YOU INTENDED.
YOU DESIGNED ME TO BE YOU, HERE. YOU MADE ME TO KEEP ORDER...
...THEN YOU TOLD ME TO LET THE NATURAL ORDER BE SPONTANEOUS.
HOW MANY CYCLES HAVE YOU BEEN GONE? HUNDREDS? I HAVE BEEN DOING MY BEST WITHOUT YOUR GUIDANCE, AND WITHOUT THE FREEDOM TO TAKE ACTION.

CLU, I DIDN'T KNOW WHAT KIND OF STRAIN THIS... NEW LIFE...WOULD PUT ON YOU.
BUT YOU HAVE TO UNDERSTAND, I CAN'T BE HERE TO GUIDE YOU FOR EVERYTHING. I HAVE TOO MUCH TO DO IN THE REAL WORLD.
THE "REAL WORLD" YOU TALK ABOUT, IT MIGHT AS WELL BE YOUR OLYMPUS.
THIS WORLD, TO ME, TO ALL OF US... THIS IS THE REAL WORLD.
WHAT ARE YOU ASKING, CLU? YOU WANT TO SEE OLYMPUS?
NO. I'M ASKING FOR THE TOOLS TO MAKE THIS WORLD INTO A HOME FIT FOR GODS.

OKAY. I CAN UNLOCK ANY LIMITS I PUT ON THE GRID.
OR, I CAN MAKE IT ALL A MOOT POINT IF I FIND THE CAUSE OF THE BUGS.
ISN'T IT OBVIOUS? THE ISOS ARE THE ROOT OF THE PROBLEM. YOU YOURSELF SAID THEY WERE NOT OF YOUR MAKING. HOW CAN WE HAVE THE PERFECT SYSTEM IF YOU DID NOT MAKE THEM?

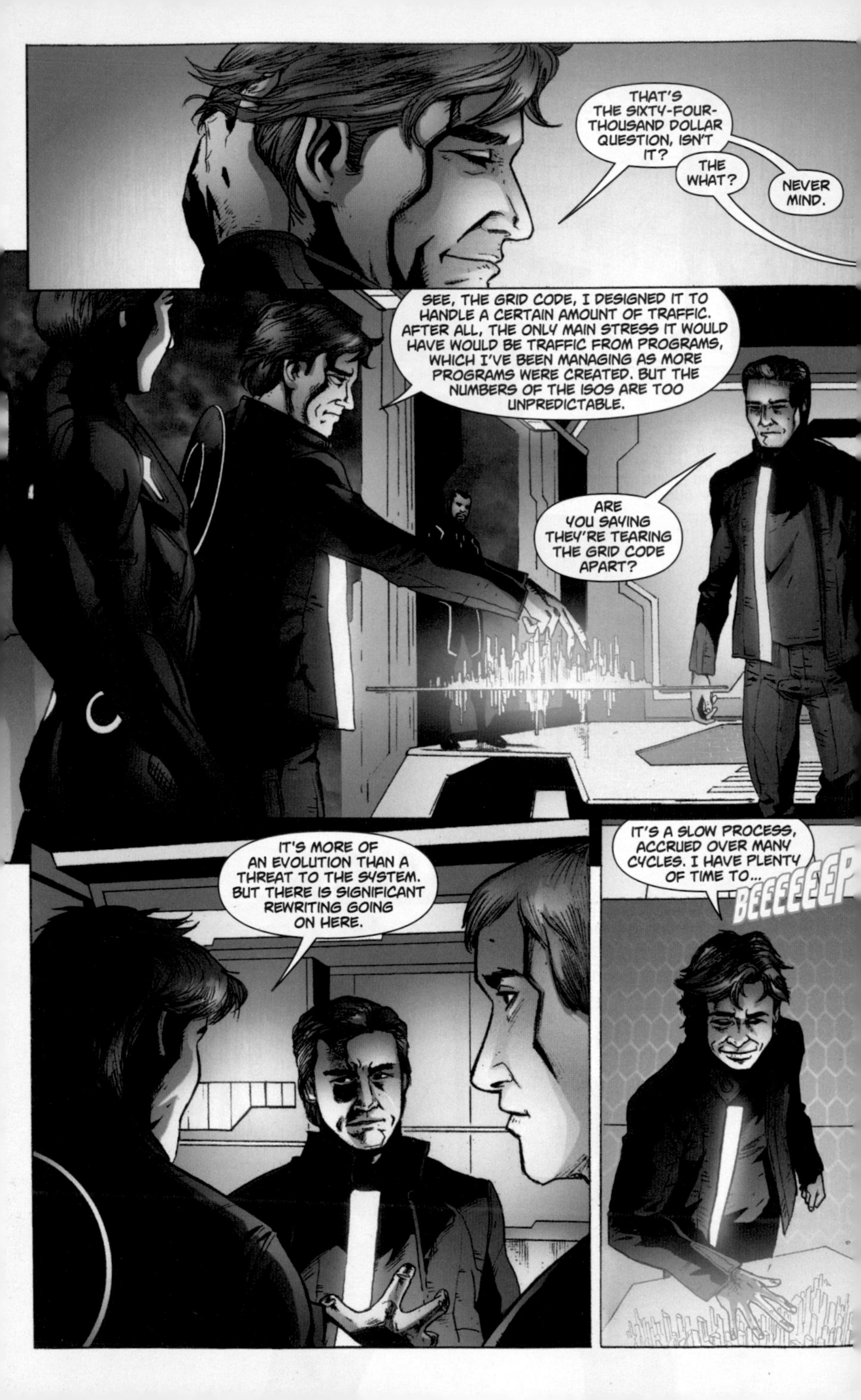
THAT'S THE SIXTY-FOUR-THOUSAND DOLLAR QUESTION, ISN'T IT?
THE WHAT?
NEVER MIND.
SEE, THE GRID CODE, I DESIGNED IT TO HANDLE A CERTAIN AMOUNT OF TRAFFIC. AFTER ALL, THE ONLY MAIN STRESS IT WOULD HAVE WOULD BE TRAFFIC FROM PROGRAMS, WHICH I'VE BEEN MANAGING AS MORE PROGRAMS WERE CREATED. BUT THE NUMBERS OF THE ISOS ARE TOO UNPREDICTABLE.
ARE YOU SAYING THEY'RE TEARING THE GRID CODE APART?
IT'S MORE OF AN EVOLUTION THAN A THREAT TO THE SYSTEM. BUT THERE IS SIGNIFICANT REWRITING GOING ON HERE.
IT'S A SLOW PROCESS, ACCRUED OVER MANY CYCLES. I HAVE PLENTY OF TIME TO...
BEEEEEEP

JORDAN.
I HAVE TO GO, FELLAS.
BUT...
NO BUTS! IT'S THE BABY.
THE WHAT?
THERE HE GOES.
BUT DID YOU SEE IT, TRON?
HE ALWAYS SAID IT WAS IMPOSSIBLE TO CONTACT THE GRID FROM HIS WORLD...

I KNOW YOU'RE FRUSTRATED, CLU, BUT IT MAKES SENSE. HE IS THE CREATOR. HE IS OF TWO WORLDS.
THE WORLD OF THE USERS, AND THE WORLD HE MADE. WE MUST FORGIVE HIM FOR NEEDING TO BE IN BOTH PLACES.
MY CONCERN IS THIS WORLD. OUR WORLD. OUR SURVIVAL MUST BE OUR PRIMARY GOAL.
YOU THINK YOU KNOW BETTER THAN HIM?
HE MADE ME IN HIS IMAGE. FOR ALL INTENTS AND PURPOSES. I *AM* THE CREATOR.
AND TOGETHER WE CAN KEEP THIS WORLD A PERFECT SYSTEM.

EMERGENCY
NO STANDING ANYTIME
LOOK OUT!
VVRRRRRRRMM

SCREEEEE

JORDAN CANAS! JORDAN CANAS! SHE'S IN LABOR AND DELIVERY! I NEED TO KNOW HER ROOM NUMBER!

MR. CANAS?
YES! WELL, NO. MR. FLYNN. I'M THE DAD.
YOU'RE JUST IN TIME.
TO CUT THE CORD.
HEY, BABE.
CONGRAT-ULATIONS, MR. FLYNN. IT'S A BOY.
WE DID IT, JORDAN. LOOK WHAT WE MADE...
ROME WASN'T BUILT IN NINE MONTHS. BUT IT'S AMAZING WHAT YOU CAN BUILD IN THAT TIME.
END OF CHAPTER ONE

+

CHAPTER TWO

BY JAI NITZ, STARLIGHT RUNNER ENTERTAINMENT, ANDIE TONG, & PETE PANTAZIS

HEY BABE. I TOLD YOU I'D BRING SAM BY ON HIS BIRTHDAY. IT WAS LAST WEEK. I'M *LATE*, LIKE NORMAL.
DADDY, CAN WE GO?
SURE, BUDDY. JUST GIVE ME A SECOND TO TALK TO MOMMY.
I MISS YOU EVERY SINGLE DAY, JORDAN.
TELL MOMMY YOU LOVE HER.

LOVE YOU, MOMMY.
ROME FELL IN A DAY.

KEVIN, THE BOARD WON'T GO FOR IT. THEY DON'T SEE A FUTURE IN INDIA.
INDIA HAS CHINA'S POPULATION WITH NO LANGUAGE BARRIER. AND THEY'RE A DEMOCRACY. WHAT'S THE PROBLEM?
DADDY, I DON'T FEEL GOOD.
JUST A MINUTE, ALAN.
AND THEY'RE THE WORLD'S LARGEST DEMOCRACY. DID I ALREADY SAY THAT?
COME HERE, KIDDO.
BARF
ALAN, LET ME CALL YOU BACK.
LET'S GET YOU SOME REST, BUDDY.

ZZZZZZZZZZZZZ
THEY'RE ASLEEP AGAIN.
LIKE FATHER, LIKE SON.
COME TO GRANDMA, BABY.
HE GOT SICK EARLIER. NEEDED A NAP.
HIM, OR YOU? IT'S ALMOST SEVEN O'CLOCK, KEVIN.
SEVEN? OH, MAN. I SLEPT THROUGH THE ENCOM BOARD MEETING. I'M TRYING TO GET THEM TO RECONSIDER MUMBAI. THEY JUST DON'T HAVE THE VISION. THEY ARE HUNG UP ON WHAT YOU CAN'T DO.
KEVIN, YOU'VE PUT A BRAVE FACE ON LOSING JORDAN, BUT MAYBE YOU SHOULD JUST STEP AWAY. MY DAUGHTER WAS OKAY WITH THE WAY YOU WORK, BUT SAM WILL ONLY BE YOUNG ONCE.
THAT'S WHY I NEED TO DO THIS. IT'S ABOUT TAKING CARE OF THE THINGS I MADE.
WHEN JORDAN WAS ALIVE IT ALL WORKED SO WELL. THERE WAS A BALANCE. ENCOM, THE GRID, HOME LIFE. IT ALL FIT TOGETHER. WE COULD DO ANYTHING.
NOW? I FEEL LIKE I'M LOSING IT ALL.

FOUR SEVENTY-SIX AD, ROME FELL.

BOTH OF YOU HOLD ON, I'VE GOT YOU!

VROOOOM
SCREEEE
ARE YOU ALL RIGHT?
YES, I THINK.
SIR, ARE YOU...
TRON, IT'S ME.
FLYNN? GOODNESS, YOU LOOK...
THAT BAD, HUH?

FLYNN, THINGS HAVE BEEN WORSE. THE TENSIONS BETWEEN CLU AND THE ISOS ARE...
SPEAK OF THE DEVIL.
I CAME AS SOON AS I HEARD, ARE YOU OKAY?
WAS IT ANOTHER ATTACK BY THE ISOS?
WE DON'T KNOW THAT THEY'RE BEHIND IT.
ARE YOU REALLY SO BLIND, TRON? YOU KNOW IT AS WELL AS I DO, THE SYSTEM WAS WORKING.
THEN THEY CAME ALONG.

COINCIDENCE ISN'T PROOF, CLU. HOW DO YOU KNOW THE ISOS ARE BEHIND ANY OF THE PROBLEMS HERE?
LOOK AROUND YOU. THEY ARE THE ONLY THING HERE YOU DIDN'T MAKE, AND THEY'RE SPREADING THROUGHOUT THE GRID. THE PROBLEMS OF THE GRID GRAVITATE TO THEM. WHAT IS IT YOU ALWAYS SAY?
IF THERE'S SMOKE, THERE'S FIRE, RIGHT?
NOW YOU'RE TRYING TO TALK LIKE HIM?
CLU, THINGS AREN'T ALWAYS NEAT AND TIDY.
NO, THEY AREN'T. SOMETIMES THINGS HAVE TO BE EXCISED TO MAKE ROOM FOR PERFECTION. YOU ASKED ME TO BUILD THE PERFECT SYSTEM. DOES THIS LOOK LIKE PERFECTION TO YOU?

THE ISO SECTION OF THE GRID TAKES MY BREATH AWAY AND REMINDS ME OF MY GOALS. MY THOUGHTS OF FALLING EMPIRES DISAPPEAR.
WHAT DO YOU HOPE TO ACCOMPLISH HERE, FLYNN?
I HAVE TO LISTEN TO CLU. I SHOULD HAVE PAID MORE ATTENTION TO THE ISOS FROM DAY ONE. IT'S BEEN TOO LONG SINCE I'VE BEEN TO ONE OF THEIR CITIES.
I DON'T THINK THEY'RE HAPPY TO SEE US.
WHAT DO YOU EXPECT? IT'S LIKE WE'RE FROM DIFFERENT PLANETS. WELL, I GUESS WE ARE.
THAT'S JUST IT. THEY WANT TO BE INDEPENDENT. THEY WANT THEIR OWN LITTLE WORLD. THEY WANT TO SPLIT AWAY FROM THE REST OF THE GRID.
IN A WAY, THEY HAVE.
I'M HAPPY TO LET THEM DEVELOP INDEPENDENTLY, BUT WE NEED TO HELP CLU FIND SOME BALANCE BETWEEN THEIR NEEDS AND HIS.

THEY'RE WAITING FOR US?
WORD GETS AROUND.
LET ME DO THE TALKING.
IT'S BEEN A LONG TIME, FLYNN.
OPHELIA, IT'S GOOD TO SEE YOU AGAIN.
FLYNN, THE SO-CALLED CREATOR. YOU LOOK SMALLER THAN I HAD IMAGINED.
THEY ARE BOTH GUESTS IN OUR CITY, GILES, BE NICE.
THEY MAY BE GUESTS, BUT ARE YOU HERE TO APOLOGIZE FOR YOUR LAPDOG, CLU?
OPHELIA DOESN'T WANT TO ACKNOWLEDGE THAT THINGS HAVE CHANGED. THAT WE'RE BETTER OFF ALONE
WE'RE NOT HERE FOR ANY OF THAT. WE'RE HERE TO TALK ABOUT THE TERRORIST ATTACKS.
YOU COME HERE TO INSULT MY PEOPLE? HAVE YOU NO SHAME?
YOUR PROGRAMS HAVE DEREZZED INNOCENTS, AND YOU HAVE THE GALL TO COME HERE AND CALL MY PEOPLE TERRORISTS?
I'M SORRY, FLYNN. BUT THIS IS A PROBLEM WE NEED TO PREPARE FOR ON OUR OWN.

THAT WENT WELL.
I'M SORRY. I SHOULD HAVE LET YOU DO THE TALKING. I'M NO DIPLOMAT.
NEITHER AM I. I'M STILL JUST IN AWE THAT THEY'RE ACTUALLY STANDING THERE. THEY'RE AMAZING.
I DIDN'T MAKE THEM, BUT I FEEL RESPONSIBLE FOR THEM.
AND I FORGOT THEIR BIRTHDAY.
IT WASN'T SUPPOSED TO BE THIS WAY.

OF COURSE, IT'S MUCH MORE COMPLICATED THAN THAT.
THIS IS IT, MAN. SENECA SAID, "LUCK IS WHAT HAPPENS WHEN PREPARATION MEETS OPPORTUNITY."
SENECA WAS A ROMAN PHILOSOPHER WHO WAS EXILED, AND LATER HE... LET'S JUST SAY IT DIDN'T END WELL.
BUT I PUT PREPARATION AND OPPORTUNITY IN ONE PLACE: THE SEA OF SIMULATION. THESE WERE THE TIDE POOLS OF EVOLUTION. THIS IS WHERE THE ISOS CAME FROM.
THIS IS WHAT I MADE, AND SOMEHOW IT MADE THEM.
IT'S BEAUTIFUL.
OH, SAM.
I SHOULD GET BACK.

ALAN, I DON'T CARE WHAT THEY THINK. NO, I DON'T THINK A PRESS CONFERENCE IS THE WAY TO GO. BECAUSE IT'S MY LIFE, THAT'S WHY.
GOOD GOOD. WHAT'S THIS ONE?
IT'S A MOTOCYCAH.
I'M SORRY. THEY HAVE IT IN THEIR HEADS THAT I'M A CASH COW.
THIS IS NO WAY TO LIVE, KEVIN. THIS IS NO WAY TO RAISE SAM. I KNOW HOW HARD THIS MUST BE. BUT YOU CAN'T DO THIS TO US AND SAM.
I KNOW YOU WANT TO BE HERE, BUT YOU NEED TO REALLY BE HERE.
I KNOW, I'M SORRY. IT'S JUST...
I JUST WISH YOU HADN'T GIVEN THEM OUR NUMBER, KEVIN. IT'S BAD ENOUGH...
RING RING RING RING RING
RING RING RING RING RING

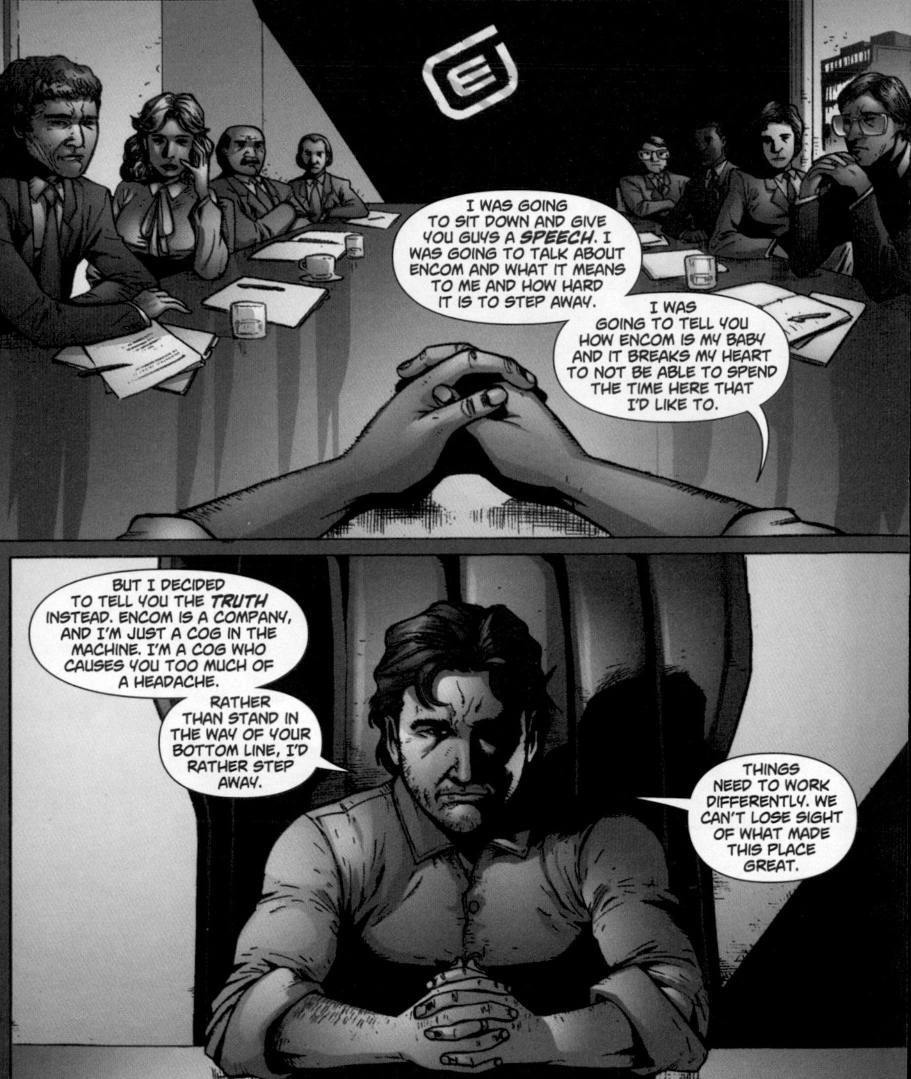
I WAS GOING TO SIT DOWN AND GIVE YOU GUYS A *SPEECH*. I WAS GOING TO TALK ABOUT ENCOM AND WHAT IT MEANS TO ME AND HOW HARD IT IS TO STEP AWAY.
I WAS GOING TO TELL YOU HOW ENCOM IS MY BABY AND IT BREAKS MY HEART TO NOT BE ABLE TO SPEND THE TIME HERE THAT I'D LIKE TO.
BUT I DECIDED TO TELL YOU THE *TRUTH* INSTEAD. ENCOM IS A COMPANY, AND I'M JUST A COG IN THE MACHINE. I'M A COG WHO CAUSES YOU TOO MUCH OF A HEADACHE.
RATHER THAN STAND IN THE WAY OF YOUR BOTTOM LINE, I'D RATHER STEP AWAY.
THINGS NEED TO WORK DIFFERENTLY. WE CAN'T LOSE SIGHT OF WHAT MADE THIS PLACE GREAT.

BUT I'M TIRED OF HEARING YOUR COMPLAINTS AND FIGHTING YOU.
THIS COMPANY WASN'T BUILT IN A DAY, AND I HAVE NO FEAR IT'LL STILL BE HERE WHEN I GET BACK. BUT MY SON NEEDS ME, SO I NEED TO TAKE A BACK-SEAT FOR A LITTLE WHILE.

THAT COULD HAVE GONE BETTER.
IT COULD HAVE GONE WORSE. AT LEAST I WASN'T LATE TO THE MEETING.
NO, YOU WERE YOUR USUAL PROFESSIONAL SELF. AREN'T YOU WORRIED THEY WON'T LET YOU BACK?
I DON'T REALLY CARE.
MY PRIORITIES DO NOT INCLUDE PLEASING A BUNCH OF POWER-HUNGRY SUITS ANYMORE. BESIDES, I'LL BE BACK BEFORE THEY KNOW IT.
I NEED TO BE THERE FOR SAM MORE THAN I NEED TO BE HERE. I CAN'T BE PULLED BETWEEN TWO WORLDS ALL OF THE TIME.
BUT THIS IS SOME VIEW, HUH?
IT SURE IS. GOOD LUCK, BUDDY.

PANG
PANG
TWAM
PANG
KRANG

ZWAM
THWANG
ZWAM
KRANG

ZWAM
CRACK
THUD

CRUNCH
WHIFF
PANG
PANG
WAM

ZWAM
STEPPING AWAY FROM ENCOM WAS A BIG CHANGE FOR ME. I IMAGINED TRON WAS GOING THROUGH THE SAME KINDS OF CHANGES THAT I WAS.

HOLD HIM STILL!
NO, DON'T!
GET AWAY FROM HIM! WHAT ARE YOU, BARBARIANS? THIS IS NOT HOW THE GAMES END!
CLU TOLD US TO DEREZZ ALL FAILED COMBATANTS. WE WERE JUST FOLLOWING ORDERS.

CLU! WE NEED TO TALK.
I THINK THIS POSITION WILL GIVE US THE OPTIMAL YIELD. YES. GO WITH THAT.
NOW!
TRON, WHAT AN UNEXPECTED PLEASURE TO HAVE YOU VISITING ME, WHAT WITH ALL THE TURMOIL ON THE STREETS AND THE VIGOROUSNESS OF THE GAMES.
THAT'S WHAT I'M HERE ABOUT. YOUR GUARDS WERE DEREZZING LOSING PROGRAMS AFTER THEIR MATCHES. DID YOU ORDER THEM TO?
YES. I DID. DO YOU WANT ME TO ALTER OUR NEW POLICY? I'D BE HAPPY TO DISCUSS IT WITH YOU.
THE GRID IS CHANGING, AND WE MUST BE THE SHEPARDS OF THAT CHANGE. WE'RE STARING INTO CHAOS, AND WE NEED ORDER. SOMETIMES, THAT MEANS FORCE.

LIKE FLYNN SAYS, WE HAVE TO BE FLEXIBLE IN THE FACE OF IMPERFECTION. IF OUR SYSTEM OF DEALING WITH LOSING PROGRAMS IN THE GAMES ISN'T PERFECT, WE MUST CHANGE IT.
WE MUST BE WILLING TO DO WHAT IT TAKES TO KEEP OUR WORLD SAFE, TRON.
THE GAMES AREN'T ABOUT FORCE, CLU. THIS IS WRONG.
I SEE YOU'RE NOT WILLING TO BUDGE, TRON.
I APOLOGIZE IF YOU FEEL I'VE GONE TOO FAR. THE GAMES WILL BE KEPT AS THEY HAVE BEEN.

KEVIN, YOU CAN'T BLAME THEM FOR BEING COLD ON THE PROPOSAL.
YOU HAVE TO ADMIT IT SOUNDS CRAZY. OIL AND COAL ARE TWO OF THE MOST ROBUST INVESTMENTS WE HAVE.
OIL IS CHOKING US, ALAN IT'S AN ENERGY ***DINOSAUR***, LITERALLY AND FIGURATIVELY.
BUT KEVIN, THINK ABOUT IT FROM THE COMPANY'S SIDE. THE DETROIT OFFICE? PITTSBURGH? NO ONE IS READY FOR THIS.
THE POPULATIONS OF DETROIT AND PITTSBURGH COMBINED FIT INTO ONE NEIGHBORHOOD IN MUMBAI.
AND TRUST ME, THE REST OF THE WORLD ARE FOLLOWING OUR LEAD. IF WE DEVOUR OIL, SO WILL THEY.
I BELIEVE YOU, BUT YOU CAN'T GO INTO A BOARD MEETING OF A FORTUNE FIVE-HUNDRED COMPANY LOOKING LIKE YOU JUST GOT BACK FROM WOODSTOCK AND TELL THEM ABOUT THE ENVIRONMENT.
I CAN CHANGE IT ALL, ALAN. ALL OF IT.
THE ENVIRONMENT? KEVIN, YOU AREN'T MAKING ANY SENSE.
NO, THE WORLD. I CAN CHANGE IT, I CAN MAKE IT BETTER.

MAN, SAM IS GETTING BIG. IT'S CRAZY HOW FAST THEY GROW. LIKE, OVERNIGHT.
IT WASN'T OVERNIGHT, KEVIN.
WHAT MY HUSBAND IS POLITELY TRYING TO SAY IS THAT YOU HAVEN'T BEEN AROUND TO WATCH SAM GROW, KEVIN.
IT HASN'T BEEN OVERNIGHT. YOU'VE JUST MISSED IT.
I'M SORRY ABOUT THAT. I REALLY AM. BUT I'VE GOT EVERYTHING FIGURED OUT NOW.
I'M STEPPING AWAY FROM ENCOM AND WORKING ON ANOTHER PROJECT. A BOOK!
IT'S ABOUT AN INTERCONNECTED WEB OF COMMUNICATION. IT'S REALLY GOING TO CHANGE EVERYTHING.
THEN I THINK I'LL TAKE SAM AND TRAVEL AROUND THE WORLD. COOL, HUH?

YEARS PASSED. SAM GOT BIGGER. I NEVER TOOK THE REINS AT ENCOM BACK. YEARS FOR ME, BUT FOR THE GRID, A LONG, LONG TIME.
VROOM
ARE YOU GUYS THE WELCOME WAGON?
GREETINGS, FLYNN. IT'S GOOD TO SEE YOU AGAIN. CLU SENT US TO BE YOUR ESCORT.
IT ISN'T SAFE FOR YOU TO BE ALONE.

CLU'S BEEN A BUSY BEE.
SO, CLU, ARE THESE GUYS GOING TO GO TO THE BATHROOM WITH ME?
ANOTHER ONE OF YOUR IDIOMS I DO NOT UNDERSTAND. BUT, I ASSUME IT HAS TO DO WITH YOUR SECURITY DETAIL. THEY ARE HERE FOR A REASON.
IT ISN'T SAFE FOR YOU TO BE ALONE.
YEAH, I HEARD THAT ALREADY. WHY ISN'T IT SAFE OUT THERE, CLU?
THE ISOS HAVE BECOME INCREASINGLY DANGEROUS. THEY ARE THE ROOT OF *ALL* OUR PROBLEMS.
YOU JUST DON'T GET IT. I THOUGHT I MADE YOU *BETTER* THAN THAT, I DON'T THINK THIS IS...

ENOUGH!
YOU THINK THIS IS EASY? YOU THINK MAINTAINING ORDER IS EASY?
YOU BUILT ME TO RUN THE SYSTEM IN YOUR ABSENCE, BUT YOU DIDN'T COUNT ON THE ISOS SPONTANEOUSLY POPPING UP.
YOU DIDN'T FACTOR IN THE POSSIBILITY OF THINGS BEING MESSY AND IMPERFECT.
BUT YOU TASKED ME WITH BUILDING THE PERFECT SYSTEM. YOU SET ME UP TO FAIL.
I DIDN'T SET YOU UP TO FAIL, CLU. SOMETIMES THE REAL WORLD IS MESSY AND IMPERFECT.
THIS ISN'T "THE REAL WORLD," FLYNN.
AND IT'S NOT THE WORLD YOU CREATED ANYMORE, EITHER.

KEEP YOUR FORMATION TIGHT. IN AND OUT QUICKLY.
CLU IS... HE'S SO MUCH LIKE ME. AND SO MUCH LIKE MY CHILD. I NEED HIM TO SEE THAT UNCERTAINTY AND EVOLUTION ARE GOOD FOR A SOCIETY. FOR THIS SOCIETY. EVEN IF IT'S NOT WHAT THE GRID WAS BUILT FOR.
GET THE BOMB SET AND MOVE OUT.
BEEP BEEP

QUICKLY, QUICKLY.
SIR, I LEFT MY BATON BACK AT THE SITE.
GO BACK AND GET IT, AND DON'T LET ANYONE SEE YOU.
BEEP BEEP
BUT THE DIFFERENCE BETWEEN CLU AND THE ISOS MIGHT BE TOO GREAT. THERE NEEDS TO BE A BALANCE.
CLICK

THIS ISN'T WHAT WE WERE MEANT FOR, SHADDOX.
YOU'RE RIGHT, TRON. IT ISN'T.
WHAT DID YOU FIND? EVIDENCE?
YOU COULD SAY THAT. IT WAS A BOMB. THE BLACK GUARD HAVE BEEN PLANTING THEM IN THE ISO OUTPOSTS.
THEY WERE AN EXPERIENCED TEAM. AND I CAN'T BELIEVE THEY COULD OPERATE WITHOUT CLU'S KNOWLEDGE.
SO WHAT ARE YOU GOING TO DO? CLU IS THE GRID. WITHOUT HIM, EVERYTHING WOULD FALL APART.
BUT IF I DO NOTHING, THE ISOS WILL FALL. COULD HE BECOME A MONSTER?

CLU IS CAST IN THE CREATOR'S IMAGE, MAYBE TOO MUCH SO.
NOW HE'S MAKING THE DECISIONS TO MATCH. WE BOTH KNOW FLYNN IS THE ONLY TRUE AUTHORITY HERE ON THE GRID. BUT CLU MAY NOT LET THAT STOP HIM.
THE BOMBINGS ARE JUST A PIECE OF A BIGGER PUZZLE. DO YOU KNOW WHAT CLU HAS PLANNED?
NO. BUT I KNOW WHAT I'D THINK. WHY ALLOW THERE TO BE MORE AND MORE ISOS? WHAT'S FLYNN SAY? "NIP THE PROBLEM IN THE BUD."
MAYBE I SHOULD CHECK CLU'S HQ AGAIN.

YOU SEE THE LAST SET OF GAMES?
I COULDN'T MAKE IT. YOU GOING TONIGHT? I HEAR TRON IS COMPETING.
YEAH, BUT HE WON'T DEREZZ ANYBODY. BORING.
NOT FOR CLU.
PANG
PANG
ZWAM

WHAT ARE YOU PLANNING...?
THIS WAS THE BOMB I STOPPED.
BUT THEN WHAT ARE THESE OTHER MARKINGS?
THE SEA OF SIMULATION?

TRON, YOU MY NEW ESCORT?
FLYNN, I THINK CLU'S GUARDSMEN ARE THE ONES PLANTING EXPLOSIVES IN THE ISO CITIES.
ON WHOSE ORDERS?
I DON'T KNOW. IT COULD BE A ROGUE ELEMENT, BUT THAT SEEMS HIGHLY UNLIKELY. BUT THAT'S NOT ALL. THEY HAVE SOMETHING PLANNED FOR THE SEA OF SIMULATION.
WE NEED TO FIND THEM.
I DON'T THINK THAT'S A GOOD IDEA TO PUT YOU IN HARM'S WAY. MAYBE I SHOULD...
NOW, TRON. I KNOW CLU IS FRUSTRATED, BUT HE'S STILL ME, I KNOW HE'LL DO WHAT'S RIGHT.
AND I'M NOT GOING TO LOSE THIS WORLD, TOO.

THE EMPIRE OF MY AMBITION WAS DIVIDED, AND I WAS TORN BETWEEN THE TWO.
I WANTED THE STABILITY OF CLU. BUT I ALSO WANTED THE UNLIMITED POSSIBILITIES OF THE ISOS. I THOUGHT THE TWO COULD COEXIST.
WHAT ABOUT THE BOMB? IT WAS SUPPOSED TO GO OFF BY NOW.
KEEP YOUR MIND ON YOUR TASK. IT'LL ALL WORK OUT...
...SOON.
VROOOOOOM

SMASH

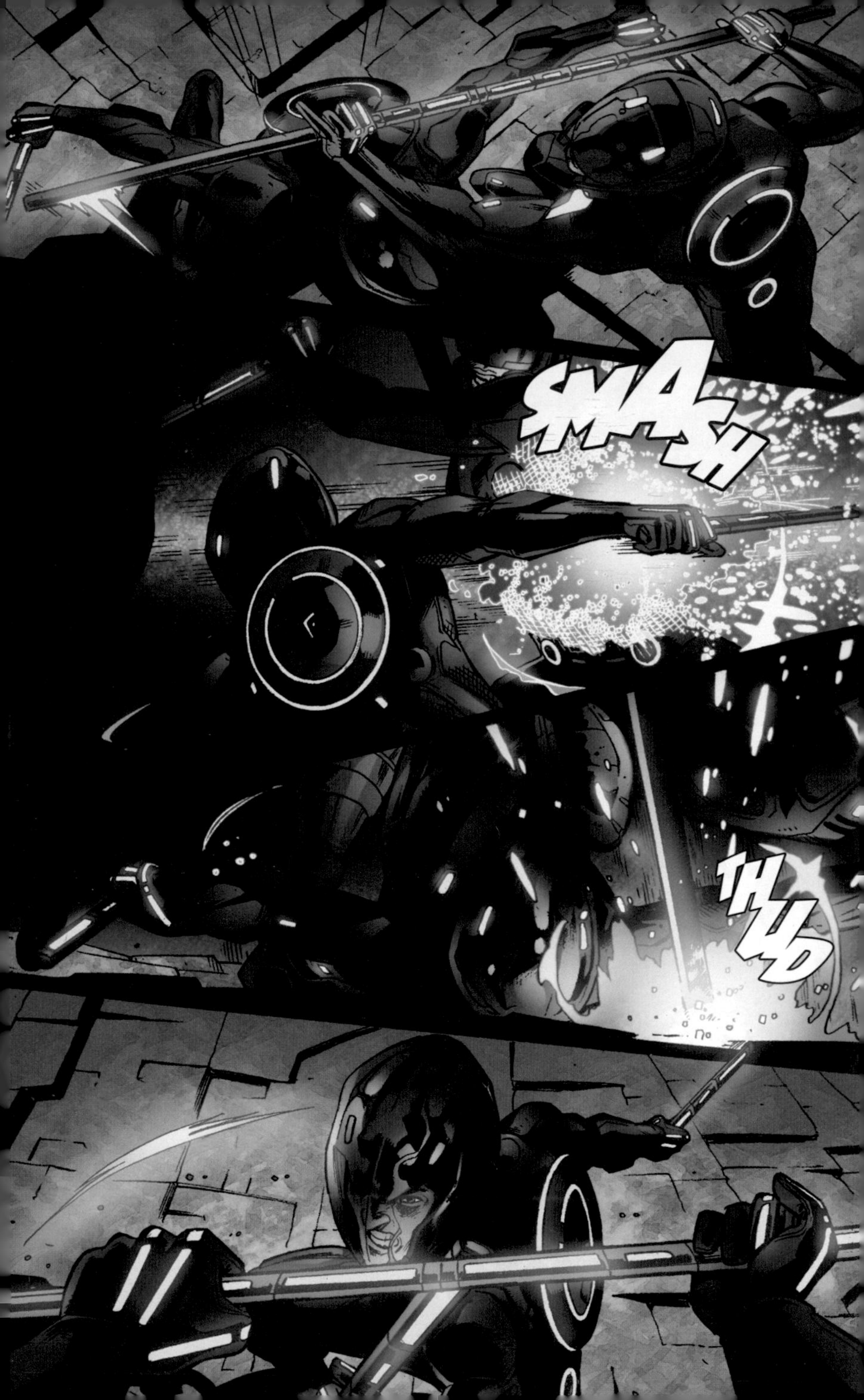
SMASH
THUD

SMASH
PANG
PANG
PANG

CLU! WHAT ARE...?
WIPE THEM OUT, MEN. THOSE MAVERICK GUARDSMEN CANNOT BE ALLOWED TO CONTINUE.
CLU? WHAT HAVE YOU DONE?
YOU THINK IT'S THAT EASY? SET UP YOUR OWN MEN AND WIPE THEM OUT?
THIS WON'T WORK, CLU.
IT ALREADY HAS, TRON.
LOOK.

YOU ARE SO SHORTSIGHTED, TRON. IT HAS TO BE THIS WAY. THE TERRORISTS ARE DEFEATED. WHO CAN ARGUE WITH THAT?
I HAVE ACTED OUT OF LOVE, TRON. I HAVE ACTED BECAUSE I CARE. I HAVE BEEN TASKED WITH PROTECTING ALL CITIZENS OF THE GRID, EVEN THE ISOS.
I AM PROTECTING US, AND THEM, FROM THEMSELVES. I WILL PROTECT THEM, BUT I WON'T LET THEM TEAR THE GRID APART.
YOU HAVEN'T SAVED ANYONE! YOU'VE JUST CREATED YOUR OWN VILLAINS AND WIPED THEM OUT. THAT ISN'T A VICTORY.
THEY COULD HAVE TAKEN CARE OF THEMSELVES! ALL YOU'VE DONE IS FORCED THE ISSUE UNTIL SOMETHING GAVE OUT. YOU PUSHED IT UNTIL IT BROKE.
CAN YOU HEAR YOURSELF?
YOU SOUND LIKE ONE OF THEM, TRON.
IS THAT WHAT YOU WANT SAID ABOUT YOU WHEN YOU'RE GONE?
ARE YOU THREATENING ME?
ENOUGH!

WHAT'S GOING ON.
HE CAN SEE IT NOW.
HE CAN SEE THE *TRUTH*.
WHAT DID THEY DO?
THEY'RE TRYING TO DESTROY SENECA.
THEY WANT TO KILL THE PLAC WHERE *IDEAS* ARE BORN. THE DIDN'T KNOW AN BETTER, SO THE TRIED TO KILL IT.

SCHOLARS AND HISTORIANS DEBATE THE ROOT CAUSES OF THE FALL OF ROME.
THEY DID IT BEFORE WE ARRIVED. THEY POISONED THE SEA OF SIMULATION.
IT'S AN ISOMORPHIC VIRUS.
"FIGHT FIRE WITH FIRE," TRON.
LOOK. IT'S THEM. THEY CAN FEEL IT.

SOME SAY IT WAS OVEREXPANSION. OTHERS SAY IT WAS THE DECLINE OF MILITARY DISCIPLINE.
CITIZENS OF THE GRID, THIS IS INDEED A DARK DAY. A GROUP OF ROGUE TERRORISTS POISONED THE SEA OF SIMULATION.
LUCKILY, THOSE TERRORISTS WERE DESTROYED SO THEY CAN HARM NO OTHERS.
ONE OF OUR MOST PRECIOUS RESOURCES HAS BEEN ATTACKED.
THIS IS A DEVASTATING BLOW, BUT I KNOW WE CAN WORK TOGETHER TO OVERCOME IT.
OTHERS SAY IT WAS THE HEDONISM OF THE ROMAN ELITE.
TOGETHER WE CAN STILL CREATE THE PERFECT SYSTEM.

WHAT DID THEY DO? WHAT'S GOING TO HAPPEN TO OUR FUTURE BROTHERS AND SISTERS?
I DON'T KNOW, OPHELIA, BUT WE'LL MAKE THIS RIGHT SOMEHOW.
IT'S NOT YOUR FAULT, FLYNN.
I'LL FIND A WAY TO MAKE IT RIGHT.
HE STILL CARES MORE ABOUT THEM.
WE ARE THE ONLY FUTURE LEFT, AND STILL HE DOESN'T CARE ABOUT THE WORLD HE CREATED.

+

EPILOGUE

BY JAI NITZ, STARLIGHT RUNNER ENTERTAINMENT,
ANDIE TONG, & PETE PANTAZIS

1989.
THE BEGINNING.

I'VE SEEN IT ALL.
COURAGE.
BETRAYAL.

EVOLUTION.
THE SPIRIT'S UNDYING FIRE.

I DON'T KNOW WHAT'S COMING, BUT I DO KNOW THE WORLD HAS CHANGED.
MAYBE IT'S TIME I CHANGED WITH IT...

GREETINGS, PROGRAMS.
WE'RE GOING TO CREATE THE PERFECT SYSTEM.
the beginning

TRON: LEGACY
THE STORY

1989

TRON! HE **FIGHTS FOR THE USERS!**

THAT'S RIGHT. TRON WAS MY FRIEND. AND TOGETHER WITH A PROGRAM I CREATED NAMED CLU...

...WE BUILT A NEW GRID FOR **PROGRAMS AND USERS**. A PLACE WHERE ALL INFORMATION WAS **FREE AND EQUAL**. IT WAS BEAUTIFUL.

AND THEN, ONE DAY, A MIRACLE HAPPENED... BUT YOU'LL HAVE TO WAIT UNTIL NEXT TIME. I MUST GO NOW.
CAN I GO WITH YOU, DAD? PLEASE! PLEASE!

"NOT NOW, SAM. BUT ONE OF THESE DAYS YOU AND I ARE GONNA CHANGE THE WORLD!"
THAT WAS THE LAST PROMISE KEVIN FLYNN MADE TO HIS SON BEFORE DISAPPEARING...
KEVIN FLYNN ENCOM CEO AND VIDEO GAME ICON DISAPPEARED
SAM FLYNN IS NOW THE LARGEST AND YOUNGEST SHAREHOLDER
HAS FLYNN JUST RUN AWAY?
ENCOM IS IN CHAOS!
AND KEVIN'S LEGACY FELL INTO THE HANDS OF A LITTLE BOY...
...WHO'S GROWN UP!
PRESENT DAY.
WWWEEEOOOOOO
ENCOM
I'M PLEASED TO ANNOUNCE ENCOM'S LAST FISCAL YEAR WAS OUR **MOST PROFITABLE** EVER...
AND TONIGHT THE TWELFTH VERSION OF OUR FLAGSHIP OPERATING SYSTEM WILL HIT THE SHELVES! ED...

THANK YOU, RICHARD. OBVIOUSLY THE IDEA OF SHARING OUR SOFTWARE OR GIVING IT AWAY FOR FREE DISAPPEARED WITH KEVIN FLYNN!
EDWARD DILLINGER JR
BUT SAM HAS OTHER PLANS! AFTER HAVING CRACKED ENCOM'S MAIN COMPUTER HE'S COPYING THE NEW SOFTWARE...
UPLOAD FILES?
YES
NO
...AND UPLOADING IT FOR FREE ON THE WEB!
UHM... NICE JUMP!
MINUTES LATER SAM REACHES THE TOP OF THE BUILDING TO PUT HIS ESCAPE PLAN INTO ACTION.
AHA! I GOT YOU NOW.
ROOF
YOU WON'T ESCAPE! ALL THE EXITS ARE SEALED!
EHY, MAN, DIDN'T ANYONE TELL YOU STEALING A SOFTWARE IS WRONG?
YOUR BOSS IS OK WITH THIS.

SURE HE IS!
WHO'S YOUR BOSS?
WHAT'S IT MATTER TO YOU? THE SECURITY CHIEF.
THAT'S NOT ACTUALLY TRUE. BECAUSE YOUR BOSS ULTIMATELY WORKS FOR THE BOARD OF DIRECTORS AND THEY WORK FOR THE SHAREHOLDERS. DO YOU KNOW WHO THE BIGGEST SHAREHOLDER IS?
I DON'T KNOW, SOME KID...
MR. FLYNN...?
NOT ANYMORE.

SWIIISSSH
BUT THIS TIME SAM'S CHUTE GETS TANGLED ON A LAMP POST AND HE LANDS BADLY!
THUD
WIIISH
LAPD
DON'T MOVE!
AFTER A FEW HOURS IN THE COUNTY JAIL, SAM RETURNS TO HIS SHIPPING CONTAINER-TURNED-APARTMENT...
DUMONT
HERE HE'S VISITED ALAN BRADLEY, HIS HER'S BEST FRIEND.
I PROMISED YOU IF I EVER GOT ANY INFORMATION ABOUT YOUR DAD, I'D TELL YOU FIRST. I GOT A PAGE LAST NIGHT...
IT CAME FROM THE ARCADE. THESE ARE THE KEYS OF THE BUILDING!

FLYNN'S ARCADE. BEFORE BECOMING ENCOM'S TOP MANAGER, KEVIN FLYNN BOUGHT THIS PLACE AND MADE IT A HANGOUT FOR TEENS WHO LOVED VIDEO GAMES...
FLYNN'S
NOW IT'S ONLY A SHUTTERED BUILDING FULL OF OLD VIDEO GAME MACHINES. BUT ONE OF THEM HIDES THE SECRET ENTRANCE TO...
TRON
...KEVIN FLYNN'S BASEMENT LAB!
CREEEKKK
THE LASER DEVICE THAT YEARS AGO SENT KEVIN FLYNN TO THE GRID, THE DIGITAL WORLD, IS STILL THERE.
Z-WAAAAAAPPP
SAM ACTIVATES THE SYSTEM A BEAM OF BLUE LIGHT SHOOT ACROSS THE ROOM AND...

HEY, WHERE AM I?
A SPOTLIGHT IS PIERCING THE GLOOM... THE GRID.
THE VEHICLE IS A RECOGNIZER, SWEEPING THE CITY IN SEARCH OF ROGUE PROGRAMS.
IDENTIFY YOURSELF, PROGRAM!
THIS PROGRAM HAS NO DISC. PROGRAMS WITHOUT DISCS SHALL BE RE-ASSIGNED. NON-PRODUCTIVE PROGRAM TO GAMING.
HEY! WAIT, WAIT!
THE SENTRY PUSHES SAM INTO THE RECOGNIZER...

...WHICH TAKES OFF!
THE VEHICLE FLIES AROUND AND THROUGH THE BUILDINGS PULSING WITH BLUE ENERGY, AND ACROSS A MASSIVE CITY. THE BEDTIME STORY HIS FATHER TOLD HIM AS A KID WASN'T JUST A STORY. IT WAS A REAL PLACE. AND NOW HE'S **INSIDE** IT.

SEND HIM TO THE GAMES!
LOOK... I NEED TO TALK TO SOMEBODY...

MINUTES LATER, SAM IS BROUGHT TO AN EMPTY CHAMBER WHERE FOUR STATUES COME TO LIFE... THE SIRENS.

THEY DRESS HIM WITH ORM-FITTING ARMOR.

THEN THEY INSERT A LUMINESCENT DISC INTO A SHEATH IN HIS ARMOR...

...AND A RECORD OF WHATEVER IS CONTAINED IN SAM'S BRAIN AND NERVOUS SYSTEM IS THEN CREATED. THIS IS THE DISC AND EVERY CREATURE IN THIS WORLD HAS THEIR OWN!

DISC ACTIVATED AND SYNCHRONIZED. PROCEED TO GAMES.
GAMES? WHAT AM I SUPPOSED TO DO?

SURVIVE!
PLATFORM 8. COMBATANTS 3 AND 11. DISC GAMES.

WHEN SAM WAS A CHILD, HE PLAYED THIS VIDEO GAME MANY TIMES, OFTEN IN DOUBLE-TEAM MODE WITH HIS FATHER.
SWIIIISSSH
NOW IT'S REAL!
AND LOSING THE GAME MEANS DEATH!

SAM HAS TO LEARN QUICKLY IF HE WANTS TO SURVIVE!
HIS ONLY HOPE IS TO PLAY... AND WIN!
SAM IS UNDER ATTACK...
HE MANAGES TO BLOCK THE BLOW AND THEN...
...COUNTER-ATTACKS!
KE-RAAASSH
BUT JUST WHEN HE THINKS HE'S SAFE...

...HE HAS TO FACE RINZLER, THE CRUELEST WARRIOR IN THE ARENA!
AND TO MAKE THINGS WORSE, THE GRAVITY ON THE PLATFORM IS REVERSED!

RINZLER IS UNSTOPPABLE!
TUMP
CRAAK
HE FIGHTS ONLY TO WIN AND DEREZZ HIS OPPONENT.
CRAAAK
BUT, SUDDENLY...
ZWIIIISHHH
A DROP OF BLOOD...
PROGRAMS DO NOT BLEED!
AND RINZLER STANDS STUNNED, UNABLE TO PROCEED WITH A DEATHBLOW!
USER...

THE UNUSUAL SCENE CATCHES THE INTEREST OF A **HELMETED FIGURE** WATCHING ON FROM A CHOICE POSITION. THIS IS AN ABNORMAL PROGRAM, INDEED!
IDENTIFY YOURSELF, **PROGRAM**!
I'M NOT A PROGRAM!
IDENTIFY YOURSELF!
MY NAME IS **SAM FLYNN**!
THE NAME ECHOES AROUND THE ARENA AND THE CROWD BEGINS TO MURMUR. FLYNN... THEY KNOW THIS NAME!
UNSEEN, ANOTHER **HELMETED FIGURE** QUICKLY EXITS...
WHILE SAM IS ESCORTED ONTO THE THRONE SHIP WHERE THE RULER OF THIS WORLD AWAITS HIM.
WHO ARE YOU?
B-ZZZZ
DAD?!

D-DAD... I GOT YOUR MESSAGE AND... I DON'T UNDERSTAND. I THOUGHT YOU WERE TRAPPED INSIDE HERE... BUT YOU'RE IN CHARGE...
...SO WHY CAN'T YOU GET OUT OF HERE?
YOU SEE, SAM. I'M NOT YOUR FATHER.
BUT I'M VERY, VERY HAPPY TO SEE YOU.
YOU... YOU ARE... CLU!
WHAT DO YOU SAY WE HAVE A LITTLE FUN?
CLU'S SHIP MOVES FROM TH BIG ARENA AND REACHES TH AMAZING CYCLE GRID.
GREETING, PROGRAMS!
FOR THE FIRST TIME SINCE OUR LIBERATION, WE HAVE A USER IN OUR MIDST! AND HE HAS THE NAME OF FLYNN! SO, WHO BEST TO BATTLE THIS SINGULAR OPPONENT? PERHAPS YOUR LIBERATOR, YOUR LUMINARY, YOUR LEADER. THE ONE WHO VANQUISHED THE TYRANNY OF THE USER SO MANY CYCLES AGO... CLU!
USER?!? WHAT'D YOU DO TO MY FATHER?

SAME THING I'M GONNA DO TO YOU!
CRUEL WORDS THAT IMPLY THE FINAL FATE OF SAM'S FATHER.
YOU WANT TO PLAY? I'LL PLAY!
LET IT BEGIN!
CLU LAUNCHES THE BATON IN THE AIR AND...
NOW THIS I CAN DO!

THE RACE STARTS! TWO TEAMS FIGHT AGAINST EACH OTHER...
IT'S A WILD GAME, EXTREMELY DANGEROUS...
B-ZZZZZOOOSH
B-ZZZZAAAP
...BECAUSE THE LIGHT WALLS THE CYCLES LEAVE BEHIND THEM ARE LETHAL!
WUUUOOOSH
B-ZZZZAAAP

SAM MUST DEFEAT CLU!
BUT HE'S THE KING OF THE GAMES ON THE GRID...
KE-RAAAKKKK
SAM REALIZES THAT HIS LIFE COULD END IN A FEW SECONDS IF HE CANNOT REACT...
...BUT HOW?

SUDDENLY...
BAAAASSSH
GET IN!
WHO ARE YOU?
HOLD ON.
THE MYSTERIOUS LIGHT RUNNER ROCKETS TOWARDS THE BORDER OF THE GAME GRID...
WOOOSSSH

...FOLLOWED BY THREE BLACKGUARD CYCLES LED BY RINZLER.
KA-BAAASH
RINZLER'S LIGHT CYCLE IS DEREZZED...
BAKAAM
... BUT HE HAS A SECOND BATON...
PULL UP, MAN!
VROOOOM
WE'LL NEVER MAKE IT!

ZWWWOOOSSSH
KE-BRAAASSSH

MADE IT!

BUMP

THEY'RE GIVING UP... ?!
NOT BY CHOICE. THEY CAN'T GO **OFF GRID**. THEY'D MALFUNCTION ON THIS TERRAIN.

WHERE ARE YOU TAKING ME?
PATIENCE, SAM FLYNN. I'M QUORRA... AND ALL YOUR QUESTIONS WILL BE ANSWERED SOON.
MEANWHILE, ON THE GAME GRID, CLU UNDERSTANDS SAM'S RESCUE HAS A STUNNING MEANING...
KEVIN FLYNN LIVES!
THE LIGHT RUNNER RACES OVER THE BLACK TERRAIN OF THE OUTLANDS...
...TOWARD AN ENORMOUS MOUNTAIN...
...AND IT'S ABOUT TO SMASH INTO THE ROCK...

...WHEN A HIDDEN ENTRANCE OPENS.
THROUGH A TUNNEL...
SAM AND QUORRA GET TO AN ELEVATOR THAT TAKES THEM TO...
...KEVIN FLYNN'S SAFEHOUSE!
QUORRA, I DREAMED OF AN OLD FRIEND... TRON. IT'S A SIGN.
DAD.
SAM?
LONG TIME.
YOU HAVE NO IDEA.
CLU HAD HIM ON THE LIGHT CYCLE GRID. I INTERVENED.

I IMAGINE YOU HAVE A LOT OF QUESTIONS.
ACTUALLY, JUST ONE.
WHY I NEVER CAME HOME...
"WELL, THOSE NIGHTS, WHEN I SAID I WENT TO THE OFFICE, I WAS COMING HERE..."
"THIS WAS A PLACE OF INFINITE POSSIBILITIES. AND TOGETHER WITH TRON AND CLU, WE WERE BUILDING A WHOLE NEW WORLD, A UTOPIA."
THEN SOMETHING HAPPENED!

THE MIRACLE YOU TOLD ME ABOUT, WHEN I WAS A KID.
YES, THE MIRACLE... YOU REMEMBER.
"THEY WERE ISOS... ISOMORPHIC ALGORITHMS. THE NEXT STEP IN EVOLUTION."
AND YOU CREATED THEM?
NO... THEY SIMPLY MANIFESTED LIKE FLOWERS IN A WASTELAND. ONE RANDOM MUTATION BECAME A CHAIN REACTION...
"THEY EVOLVED BEYOND MY COMPREHENSION..."
"...PROFOUNDLY NAÏVE AND UNIMAGINABLY WISE. EVERYTHING I'D HOPED TO FIND IN THE SYSTEM, CONTROL, ORDER, PERFECTION, NONE OF IT MEANT A THING! THE ISOS WERE MY GIFT TO THE WORLD. THEY WERE GOING TO CHANGE EVERYTHING."
SO WHAT HAPPENED?
CLU HAPPENED!

"WHAT I SAW AS A MIRACLE, HE SAW AS A VIRUS, AN IMPERFECTION."
FLYNN, AM I STILL TO BUILD THE PERFECT SYSTEM?
YEAH...
"HE WENT FOR MY DISC... THE KEY TO THE KINGDOM. IT WAS A COUP..."
"HE THOUGHT I HAD BEEN CORRUPTED..."
"...SO HE DECIDED I MUST BE ELIMINATED."
FLYNN, GO!
"TRUE TO HIS REPUTATION, TRON FOUGHT FOR ME TO HIS VERY END..."
"I NEVER SAW HIM AGAIN!"

IT WAS THE LAST NIGHT I EVER SAW YOU.
CLU THOUGHT YOU'D LOST THE VISION.
HE SAW THE ISOS AS MUTANTS... AN IMPERFECTION. SO HE SOUGHT TO DESTROY THEM.
WHY DIDN'T YOU FIGHT?
HE DID.
CLU FED ON MY RESISTANCE. THE MORE I FOUGHT, THE MORE POWERFUL HE BECAME.
HIS FIRST ACT WAS THE ELIMINATION OF THE ISOS.
THE PURGE.
HE KILLED THEM ALL?
IT WAS GENOCIDE.

SAM, I TRIED TO COME HOME. LOOK AT THAT LIGHT... THE PORTAL!
IT CONNECTS OUR WORLD TO THIS ONE AND AS A FAIL-SAFE, I'D SET THE DOOR TO OPEN ONLY FROM THE OUTSIDE...
...AND ONLY FOR A LIMITED TIME. THUS, THE NIGHT CLU TOOK THE POWER, I HAD NO TIME TO REACH THE PORTAL AND IT CLOSED ON ME.
BUT I ACTIVATED IT WHEN I CAME IN. SO IT'S OPEN NOW AND WE CAN GO. GET YOU OUT OF HERE.
SAM, DON'T RUSH.
WHAT DO YOU MEAN? THE PORTAL IS OPEN, BUT NOT FOR LONG... SO, WHAT?
THE MOMENT FLYNN'S ON THE GRID CLU WILL STOP AT NOTHING TO OBTAIN HIS DISC.
MY DISC IS THE MASTER KEY. THE WAY OUT. AND NOT JUST FOR ME. CLU FIGURES IF I CAN BE IN...
...HE CAN BE OUT!

SO... WE JUST DO NOTHING?
BELIEVE ME. THERE'S NO MOVE WE CAN MAKE THAT CLU HASN'T CONSIDERED. **NOTHING HAPPENS UNLESS HE WANTS IT TO.**

THAT'S NOT TRUE. LOOK AT US. WE'RE HERE.

YES... AND TELL ME, WHAT BROUGHT YOU HERE, TO THE GRID?
ALAN TOLD ME HE GOT A PAGE FROM **YOU**. AND I CAME.

I DIDN'T SEND ANY PAGE, SAM. IT WAS CLU. THIS IS ALL **HIS DESIGN**... HAVING YOU AND ME TOGETHER HEADING FOR THE PORTAL.

IT'S HIS GAME NOW. AND THE ONLY WAY TO WIN IS NOT TO PLAY!
THAT'S A HELL OF A WAY TO LIVE.

MINUTES LATER...
HOW CAN HE BE SO AFRAID OF HIS OWN CREATION? HE BUILT CLU. WHY CAN'T HE JUST END HIM?
HE COULD, BUT IT WOULD REQUIRE REINTEGRATION. YOUR FATHER WOULD NEVER SURVIVE THE EVENT.
IT WOULD BE THE END OF THEM BOTH.
WELL, IF HE REFUSES TO SAVE HIMSELF, THEN I WILL!
CLU WANTS MY FATHER'S DISC, NOT MINE. SO, I'LL REACH THE PORTAL, GO THROUGH IT, FIND ALAN AND STOP THIS THING FROM THE OTHER SIDE.
BUT I CAN'T GET OUT UNLESS SOMEONE GETS ME TO THE PORTAL - AND I BET YOU DON'T WANT TO BE STUCK HERE FOR ETERNITY EITHER.
TAKE THIS. ONCE I KNEW A PROGRAM NAMED ZUSE WHO FOUGHT ALONGSIDE THE ISOS. THEY SAY HE MANAGES THE DISSIDENT FACTIONS AND HE CAN GET ANYONE... ANYWHERE.

AND SO, SAM LEAVES HIS FATHER'S SAFEHOUSE AND RACES TOWARD THE OLD CITY...
UNFORTUNATELY A SENTRY NOTICES THE WHITE BLUR LEFT BY KEVIN'S OLD CYCLE, WHICH SAM HAS STOLEN...
...AND THE NEWS QUICKLY REACHES CLU.
SIR, THE SENTRIES DOWNTOWN TRACED FLYNN'S CYCLE TO ITS POINT OF ORIGIN.
BUT KEVIN IS AWARE OF SAM'S DEPARTURE TOO. AND HE HAS MADE HIS DECISION.
YOU CAN'T GO. HE'LL BE OKAY. I SENT HIM TO SOMEONE WE CAN TRUST.
I DON'T EXPECT YOU TO UNDERSTAND. BUT NOW THERE'S NO OTHER CHOICE.

MEANWHILE, SAM REACHES THE END OF LINE CLUB...

...HE GIVES HIS CYCLE TO A DESTITUTE PROGRAM IN EXCHANGE FOR A PONCHO TO DISGUISE HIMSELF.

BUT THERE'S SOMEONE WHO RECOGNIZES HIM.

FORTUNATELY SHE'S A FRIEND, NOT A FOE...
I CAN HELP YOU, SAM FLYNN...
...AND INTRODUCES SAM TO THE END OF LINE CLUB'S PROPRIETOR.
HIS NAME'S CASTOR. IF YOU WANT TO SPEAK TO ZUSE, YOU HAVE TO GO THROUGH HIM.
THE SON OF FLYNN! I'M AT YOUR SERVICE!
PERHAPS WE SHOULD GO TO MY PRIVATE LOUNGE. BUT FIRST...
BOYS, CHANGE THE SCHEME, ALTER THE MOOD, ELECTRIFY THE CROWD!

IN THE MEANTIME, CLU AND HIS GUARDS HAVE REACHED KEVIN'S SAFEHOUSE, HOPING TO CATCH HIM AND HIS SON. BUT IT'S EMPTY AND ABANDONED...
YET IT IS FULL OF MEMORIES... A PLACE CLU IS SEEING NOW, AFTER SO MANY YEARS.
YOU ARE CLU. YOU ARE TO CREATE THE PERFECT SYSTEM.
CLU REMEMBERS THE MOMENT OF HIS BIRTH... AND HIS FATHER'S FACE!
AAARRGH!
THEN SOMETHING CATCHES CLU'S ATTENTION: UNFORTUNATELY, CASTOR'S ORDER TO HIS DJS WAS NOT SIMPLY A MEANS OF PROVIDING ENTERTAINMENT FOR HIS GUEST...
...BUT A SIGNAL TO CLU MEANING "SAM FLYNN IS HERE!"

MOVE.
BACK TO CASTOR'S SANCTUARY...
SO WHEN DO I MEET ZUSE?
YOU JUST DID.
AFTER THE PURGE I NEEDED TO REINVENT MYSELF, YOU UNDERSTAND. NOW, WHAT CAN I DO FOR YOU?
I NEED TO GET TO THE PORTAL. CAN YOU HELP ME?
OF COURSE.
YOU'LL NEED TO CHANGE YOUR ATTIRE, YOU'LL NEED A FORGED DISC...
THIS IS GOING TO BE QUITE THE RIDE.
HEY, WHAT THE...?!

E-RAAASH
YOU... BETRAYED ME!
I BELIEVED IN USERS ONCE BEFORE, BUT THE GAME HAS CHANGED.
CLU'S GUARDS STORM INTO THE CLUB...
...BURSTING INTO PURE CHAOS.
ZAAAAPPP

A GROUP OF PROGRAMS WHO JOINED THE REBELLION AGAINST CLU, LED BY THE ONE NAMED BARTIK...
YAAAH!
...FIGHT TRYING TO PROTECT SAM...
...BUT UNSUCCESSFULLY!
AAAAH!
ZWAAASH
BEHOLD THE SON OF FLYNN! BEHOLD THE SON OF OUR MAKER!

SAM IS TRYING TO ESCAPE, BUT SOMEBODY WANTS TO STOP HIM...
LUCKILY, ANOTHER FIGHTER BREAKS IN, DEFLECTING THE DISC.
KLAAACK
QUORRA, FURIOUS AND FIGHTING TO SAVE SAM!
SAM AND QUORRA MAKE THEIR WAY TOWARD THE EXIT...
...BUT THERE ARE TOO ANY GUARDS AND THEY ARE QUICKLY OVERWHELMED...

...WITH A TRAGIC CONCLUSION.
ZWAAASH
...AAAH!
ALL HOPE SEEMS LOST.
BUT IN THAT VERY MOMENT...
...THE MAKER OF THAT WORLD APPEARS AMONG HIS CREATIONS, ABSORBING THE ENERGY OF THE ROOM BY TOUCHING THE FLOOR! EVERYBODY STOPS.
KEVIN FLYNN!
HE'S HERE!
IT'S HIM!

BUT NOT ALL CLU'S GUARDS ARE SO STUNNED BY KEVIN'S ARRIVAL...

THONK

...AND WITH A QUICK SHOT, A BLACK GUARD YANKS **KEVIN'S DISC** OFF HIS BACK!

CLACK

BUT THE BLACK GUARD WHO STOLE FLYNN'S DISC...
...WILL HAVE NO PRIZE...
ACKKK!
THANK YOU!

MEANWHILE...

...KEVIN ACCESS THE PANEL, PROGRAMMING THE ELEVATOR AND BRINGING IT...

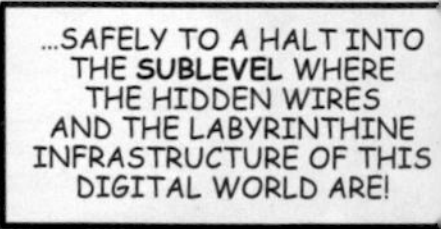
...SAFELY TO A HALT INTO THE **SUBLEVEL** WHERE THE HIDDEN WIRES AND THE LABYRINTHINE INFRASTRUCTURE OF THIS DIGITAL WORLD ARE!

SCREEEEN

DAD, YOUR DISC... IT'S GONE! BUT WE CAN GO BACK. I CAN GO BACK!
NO, THIS IS THE ROAD WE'RE ON NOW. WE HEAD TO THE PORTAL. LET'S CLIMB INTO THE HULL OF THAT **SOLAR SAILER!**

"IT WILL TAKE US EAST... TO THE PORTAL!"
MEANWHILE, AT THE END OF LINE CLUB, CLU ARRIVES AFTER KEVIN AND SAM HAVE ESCAPED...
YOUR EXCELLENCY, I **PRESUME** THE BOY AND KEVIN PERISHED IN THE ELEVATOR.
TLACK
YOU PRESUME? **RINZLER, GO!**
TLACK
NOW... THE DISC... GIVE IT TO ME.
I **PRESUME** OUR UNDERSTANDING IS STILL VALID: I'LL HAVE CONTROL OF THE CITY.
DON'T PRESUME.
BLIP BLIP

BOOM
RINZLER FINDS TRACES OF KEVIN FLYNN'S PASSAGE...
...AND REALIZES THAT THE FLYNNS HAVE ESCAPED ABOARD A SOLAR SAILER. HE TAKES CHASE.
IN THE MEANTIME, CLU PREPARES THE NEXT STEP OF HIS PLAN...
SET COURSE FOR THE RECTIFIER.
ON THE SOLAR SAILER, KEVIN FLYNN MUST PERFORM VIRTUAL SURGERY ON QUORRA TO SAVE HER LIFE.
I HAVE TO IDENTIFY THE DAMAGED CODE... BUT IT'S ENORMOUSLY COMPLEX... JUST BEYOND ME... I DIDN'T WRITE IT...

DO YOU MEAN... SHE'S AN ISO?
THE LAST ISO.
AND NEVERTHELESS SHE RISKED HERSELF FOR ME...
SOME THINGS ARE WORTH THE RISK. HAH! DONE!
MINUTES LATER...
QUORRA, YOU'RE OKAY. AND WE'RE SAFE FOR NOW, HEADED TOWARDS THE PORTAL.
THE PORTAL... I'VE NEVER BEEN SO CLOSE BEFORE. IT'S HOW I IMAGINE SUNRISE.
TRUST ME, THERE'S NO COMPARISON.
WHAT'S IT LIKE?
THE SUN? OH, MAN. I'VE NEVER DESCRIBED IT BEFORE. WARM... RADIANT...

BEAUTIFUL.
SUDDENLY, THE SOLAR SAILER SHIFTS ITS COURSE...
B-ZZZZSSSSH
...AND IT'S ATTRACTED TOWARDS THE RECTIFIER, PREPARING TO DOCK.
IT IS A MILITARY BASE WHERE CLU BUILDS HIS ARMY IN SECRET...

...USING CAPTIVE PROGRAMS THAT ARE TRANSPORTED HERE IN CONTAINERS ABOARD THE CARGO SAILERS...
M306
...AND RE-PURPOSED TO BECOME CLU'S DRONE SOLDIERS!
A TERRIBLE FATE THAT QUORRA IS PREPARED TO RISK...
...WHEN SHE DECIDES TO DISTRACT RINZLER, WHO IS SEARCHING FOR THEM.

BUT WHILE THE FLYNNS ARE FLEEING, KEVIN LOOKS AT RINZLER'S FIGHTING POSITION AND HE RECOGNIZES HIS OLD FRIEND'S STYLE...
"TRON, WHAT HAVE YOU BECOME!"
...AND HE UNDERSTANDS THE TRUTH: CLU DID NOT KILL TRON THAT INFAMOUS NIGHT. HE REPROGRAMMED HIM!
MOTTL

BUT THERE'S NO TIME TO MOURN FOR HIS FRIEND...
THOSE JETS! THEY'RE OUR WAY OUT!
A MOMENT LATER, RINZLER TAKES HIS PRECIOUS PREY TO CLU.
AN ISO! HOW TRAGIC TO BE THE LAST... OF THE MIRACLE.
CLU, I'VE SEEN WHAT THE USERS ARE CAPABLE OF AND YOU DON'T DESERVE TO BE WITH THEM.
TAKE HER UPSTAIRS AND FIND SAM AND KEVIN FLYNN. NOW I HAVE TO TALK TO MY PEOPLE.
FELLOW PROGRAMS, THERE WAS A TIME WHEN WE BELIEVED THAT THIS WORLD WAS ALL THERE WAS! BUT NOW WE POSSESS THE KEY TO THE WORLD OF OUR CREATOR!
WE WILL RID IT OF IMPERFECTION! OUT THERE IS OUR VICTORY... OUR DESTINY!

HE WANTS TO INVADE OUR WORLD! WE HAVE TO GET YOUR DISC.
NO! WE MUST BEAT HIM TO THE PORTAL. YOU'LL PASS THROUGH IT AND SHUT HIM DOWN FROM THE OUTSIDE.
BUT BY THE TIME I MAKE IT, YOU'LL BE LONG GONE! YOUR DREAM IS STILL POSSIBLE, DAD... AND I'LL HELP YOU MAKE IT REAL.
WHAT ARE YOU GOING TO DO?
AND WHAT ABOUT QUORRA? NO, I'M NOT GOING BACK ALONE. SOME THINGS ARE WORTH THE RISK!
I'M A USER. I'LL IMPROVISE
THEIR EYES LOCK IN A MOMENT OF PERFECTLY UNDERSTANDING. THE STUDENT HAS BEGUN TO TEACH THE TEACHER. THEY SET OFF IN OPPOSITE DIRECTIONS.

KEVIN USES HIS KNOWLEDGE OF THIS WORLD TO REPROGRAM A SENTRY...
WHAT ARE...
I'M TAKING THIS VEHICLE!
RIGHT AWAY, SIR! WATCH YOUR STEP AS YOU BOARD THE AIRCRAFT.
AND IN THE SAME INSTANT, THE ELEVATOR REACHES CLU'S SHIP WHERE KEVIN'S DISC IS SET...
THE ELEVATOR SEEMS TO BE EMPTY...
WOOOSH
BUT IT ISN'T!

THUD
AAAKKK!
THE PRIZE FOR SAM'S BRAVE ACTION IS KEVIN'S DISC...
GOT IT! AND NOW...
YOU... WHERE IS THE GIRL? THE PROGRAM I CAME IN WITH!
SAM!
...AND A FIGHT FOR QUORRA'S LIFE!
SAM! GO!
!
WHIIIP
TLOK
SWOOOSH

YOU'RE NOT THE ONLY ONE FIGHTING DOUBLE-DISC MODE!
CRAAANK
AAAGGHHH!
THUD
COME ON, KIDDO, HURRY UP!
KE-RAAASH
THUD

SAM, WHERE'D YOU LEARN THAT MOVE?
ENCOM TOWER, A COUPLE OF NIGHTS AGO!
WOOOSH
LET'S GO!
MEANWHILE, ON THE THRONE SHIP...
KEVIN FLYNN'S DISC... GONE.
THUD
SIR, I CAN EXPLA... AAAKKK!
LET'S FOLLOW THEM!

WOOOSH
AND SO, THE WILD HUNT BEGINS...
SWOOOSSSH
...AND RINZLER QUICKLY JOINS THE FORMATION WITH HIS OWN LIGHT JET.
HERE... YOU'RE GOING TO NEED IT!
THANKS, SON.
HERE THEY COME!

"SAM, TAKE THE TURRET!"
THE FIRST OF CLU'S BLACK GUARDS IS QUICKLY DEREZZED...
BUT CLU AND RINZLER CRISS-CROSS IN FRONT OF KEVIN'S JET TO CREATE A BARRIER OF LIGHT...
WOOOSH
...WHICH QUORRA DESTROYS WITH A BLAST...
KRA-KOOOM
...JUST IN TIME TO RAM A SECOND JET, WHICH CRASHES INTO A NEARBY ROCK.
KRA-KOOOM
ONE BY ONE THE BLACK GUARDS' JETS ARE DESTROYED...

...UNTIL ONLY TWO JETS CONTINUE THE HUNT: CLU'S AND RINZLER'S.
WHEN SAM TRIES TO FIRE AT RINZLER, HIS GUN JAMS!
CLACK
RINZLER HAS THE SHOT, ALL HE HAS TO DO IS PULL THE TRIGGER...
...BUT HIS EYES AND SAM'S LOCK...
...AND AN ECHO OF TRON EMERGES FROM HIS MIND. RINZLER DOESN'T SHOOT.
I FIGHT FOR THE USERS!
KA-BAAAM
IN THAT VERY MOMENT RINZLER'S JET EXPLODES, THROWING HIM OUT TOWARDS THE SEA BELOW.

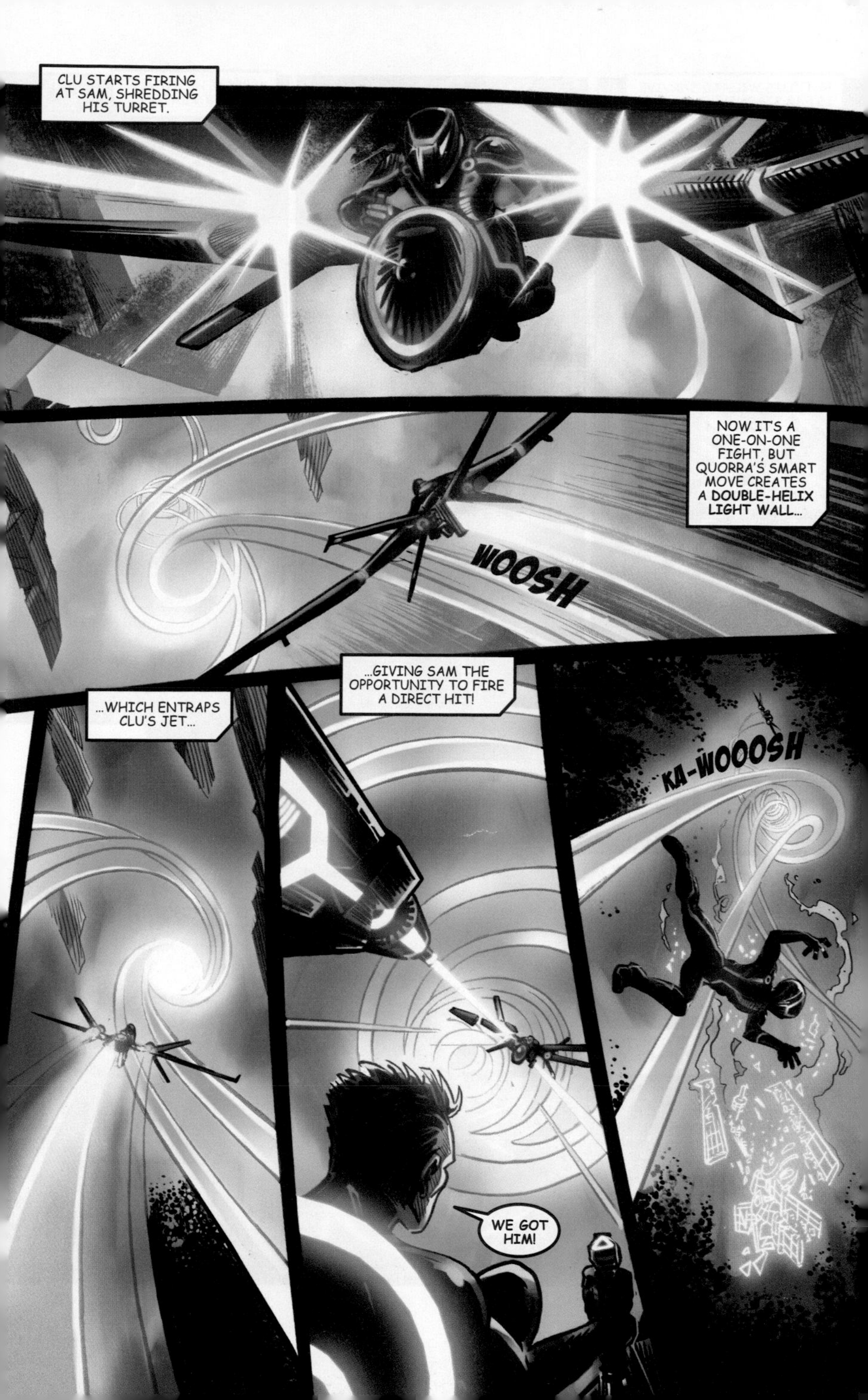
CLU STARTS FIRING AT SAM, SHREDDING HIS TURRET.
NOW IT'S A ONE-ON-ONE FIGHT, BUT QUORRA'S SMART MOVE CREATES A **DOUBLE-HELIX LIGHT WALL**...
WOOSH
...WHICH ENTRAPS CLU'S JET...
...GIVING SAM THE OPPORTUNITY TO FIRE A DIRECT HIT!
KA-WOOOSH
WE GOT HIM!

BUT CLU'S WILL TO SURVIVE IS FAR STRONGER THAN HIS LOYALTY TOWARD HIS MEN...
AND SO, HE STEALS RINZLER'S BATON...
WOOSH
...TO CREATE A NEW JET AROUND HIMSELF...
...AND CONTINUE THE HUNT!

MEANWHILE, QUORRA HAS ALMOST REACHED THE PORTAL.
PREPARE FOR CRASH LANDING!
KRA-KOOOM
TIME IS RUNNING OUT!
LOOK! THE ISLAND'S DISINTEGRATING AS THE PORTAL CLOSES!
WHEN THE TIME COMES, I NEED YOU TO DO SOMETHING FOR ME.

TO THE BRIDGE. HURRY!

BUT...
CLU! I HAD A FEELING YOU'D BE HERE.
I DID EVERYTHING YOU EVER ASKED... I TOOK THE SYSTEM TO ITS MAXIMUM POTENTIAL.
I WAS CREATING THE PERFECT SYSTEM.
YOU SEE, THE THING WITH PERFECTION IS THAT IT'S UNKNOWABLE... IT'S IMPOSSIBLE... YET IT'S IN FRONT OF US ALL THE TIME.
YOU WOULDN'T KNOW THAT BECAUSE I DIDN'T WHEN I CREATED YOU.

I'M SORRY.
SLAAAMMM
NOOO!
QUORRA, GO! IT'S TIME!

SWISSSH
CLU, IT'S ME YOU WANT.
YOU KNEW I'D BEAT YOU AND YOU STILL DID THIS... FOR HIM? WHY?
HE'S MY SON.
BUT YOUR DISC IS MINE NOW!
QUORRA GAVE HER DISC TO KEVIN WHEN THEY ENTERED THE RECTIFIER BASE...
WHAT... THIS IS... QUORRA'S DISC!
IT'S OVER, CLU!

SAM, IT'S TIME FOR YOU TO GO.
NO. I'M NOT LEAVING YOU.
SAM, IT'S WHAT HE WANTS.
SAM... IT'S TIME. TAKE HER!
SAM UNDERSTANDS. FOR A GREATER CAUSE HE MUST ACCEPT HIS FATHER'S DECISION.

NOOOOO!
CLU UNDERSTANDS THAT THE END OF HIS EVIL PLAN IS NEAR, BUT HE CAN'T ACCEPT DEFEAT. SO HE JUMPS TOWARD SAM AND QUORRA TO STOP THEM!
BUT THERE'S NO MORE TIME FOR CLU'S DREAMS OF DOMINATION...
...AS KEVIN FLYNN, CREATOR OF THIS WORLD, USES ALL HIS POWER TO CREATE A MASSIVE FORCEWAVE OF ENERGY...
SWIIIRL

...WHICH ENSNARES CLU AND BREAKS HIM DOWN TO HIS **DIGITAL ESSENCE**...
...CAUSING HIM TO MERGE WITH THE CREATOR AND HIS AVATAR!
WOOOSH
THERE'S A BLAST OF PURE LIGHT, THEN SILENCE...
BLIP BLIP
...AND A BLINKING BLUE LIGHT...

...REVEALING THAT SAM IS DOWNLOADING ALL THIS DATA ONTO A MICRODRIVE...
TRANSFER CO

...THAT HE'LL ALWAYS TAKE WITH HIM!

HE'S RETURNED TO OUR WORLD, AT LAST.

TO THE ARCADE, WHERE EVERYTHING STARTED...

...AND WHERE ALAN BRADLEY HAS COME TO MEET HIS BEST FRIEND'S SON.
YOU PAGED ME, SAM?
YEAH, I NEED YOU AT ENCOM AT 8 A.M.

YOU'RE CHAIRMAN NOW. I'M TAKING THE COMPANY BACK. WE'RE GOING TO MAKE ENCOM WHAT MY FATHER ALWAYS WANTED IT TO BE.

BUT FIRST, I HAVE SOMETHING TO DO!

WHAT'S NEXT?

COME ON...

ENCOM
I WANT TO SHOW YOU SOMETHING!
THE EN